Collected Writings of Edward Bach

(1886–1936)

Collected Writings of Edward Bach

Edited by Julian Barnard

Ashgrove Press, Bath

Published in Great Britain by
ASHGROVE PRESS LIMITED
Bath Road, Norton St Philip
Bath BA3 6 LW

First Ashgrove Press edition 1994
Reprinted 1998

ISBN 1–85398–073–0

This collection first published by
Flower Remedy Programme

See Textual notes for first date of publication, title and
publisher of all previously published material

Set in 10pt Imprint
by Quorum Technical Services, Cheltenham
Printed by Redwood Books, Trowbridge, Wilts

Contents

Foreword

There is, I suppose, a natural curiosity about what Dr Bach would be doing if he were still alive today. Some might imagine that he would be discovering new Remedies. But I do not think so, personally, because he completed his discoveries this time round. He knew that, as far as he was concerned, there were no further Remedies to be added to the 38.

So, having the 38 Remedies as a complete system of Healing, where would he devote his amazing amount of creative energy? He was a fine articulator of the written word and no less of the spoken one, as we can see from his lectures and writings that are published together in this volume. Coupled with his great desire that everyone should know and be able to use these simple Healing Herbs, it might well be that he would create the means whereby this objective could be accomplished.

I think that through the Bach Educational Programme we have such a means to further the understanding of Bach's work on a wider base through self-knowledge and awareness. Bach said all there was to say about the Remedies . . . but his words can only be helpful if we really *listen* with our hearts. The Bach Educational Programme endeavours to enable us to attune ourselves more closely to the simple truths of the message – so that eventually the gentle admonishment to *Free Thyself – Heal Thyself* will become the focus of daily living.

Nickie Murray
Sotwell, December 1986

Preface

Edward Bach (1886–1936) was a pioneer in medical research. He trained in London at University College Hospital and worked as Assistant Bacteriologist there during the Great War. His discoveries in connection with intestinal bacteria were an important contribution to contemporary medicine. He worked with F.H. Teale and their findings in this subject were recorded in the *Proceedings of the Royal Society of Medicine* during 1920. However, it was not until he joined the London Homœopathic Hospital in March 1919 that he began to develop this work in a way that was to make him famous. The story of Dr Bach's career is told in Nora Weeks' biography* but it can be seen in outline through the published papers that are brought together here under the title of *Collected Writings*.

This collection is representative rather than complete. Bach destroyed most of his research notes and only fragments remain. Technical publications have been included only where Bach was the sole author and so his book *Chronic Disease a Working Hypothesis* (1925) written jointly with Dr C.E. Wheeler has not been included. However, all the important milestones in his researches are here and can be viewed for the first time as a whole. Of particular interest to homœopaths will be his writings from the 1920s when he developed the bacterial types, known as the Bach Nosodes. The stages in his discovery of the flower remedies, for which he is world famous, are also shown. This represents a fascinating opportunity to see how his work progressed from 1928 until his death.

Sometimes these writings appear a little confusing but they are always working with Bach's two great ideals: to find simple herbal remedies that are available freely for all people to help themselves and

*Weeks, N. *The Medical Discoveries of Edward Bach, Physician*, C.W. Daniel Co.

to share his discoveries with his fellows as soon as he had made them. His urge to make things simple made his statements economical and it can be seen that, in *The Twelve Healers*, he was constantly refining his descriptions of the remedy states and the introduction to the subject.

Here, too, we can view alongside each other the development of his medical researches and his philosophical outlook. It remains to be seen whether Bach will be remembered eventually more for his flower remedies or for his perception of the nature of life. To some the healing herbs are less significant than the understanding of emotional states that informs them. Certainly they would not have been found without that understanding.

The arrangement of the material, as far as possible, has been made in reverse chronological order. At the front of the book we have his last public lecture given two months before he died. Following this are a selection of his letters and notes written in the last years. The various forms of *Twelve Healers* are all given in full. The 1936 edition of *The Twelve Healers & Other Remedies* is not the final one since a different introduction, written by Bach, was inserted after his death in the 1941 edition. This can be read in the currently published version* where the introduction and main text are original and written by Bach. Notes at the back have been added at different stages. In 1979 Dr Bach's own description of how to make the remedies was removed.

Earlier writings of Bach's appeared in journals of the day like *Homœopathic World*. Curiously this was to be retitled as *Heal Thyself* in 1933, a borrowing of Bach's title for his book published in 1931. J. Ellis Barker printed several articles on Bach's work. His comments are of interest. In an editorial he wrote that "Dr Bach's assertions are staggering" and that he could well understand that the medical profession received them with "ridicule and derision". It was in this same magazine that two articles on the remedies were written by Nora Weeks, "from a lay point of view". It is evident that Bach felt that she had written a good account of the work. Here too, was Victor Bullen writing a letter from Cromer recounting how Dr Bach had helped a friend who had been partially paralysed and how his own headaches, acute depression and tremendous fear had been helped by the Remedies.

*The Twelve Healers & Other Remedies, 1983, C.W. Daniel Co.

Further back in time, transcripts of talks given at the Homœopathic Society, London, and the International Homœopathic Congress were published in *The British Homœopathic Journal*. These are rather technical and perhaps obscure to the general reader. They point to the way that Bach progressed from the complexity of professional debate to the simple universal statements of human experience.

When Bach left London in 1930 he left behind a maturing career in medicine and sought a fresh and living view of existence. He found it, as we know. The change in Bach during his working life was constant. Not that he was restless, more that he was unwilling to rest with accepted truths. He was always searching for a deeper understanding.

Julian Barnard

Public Lecture

IN THE

MASONIC HALL, WALLINGFORD,

ON

Thursday, Sept. 24th

AT 8 P.M.,

Healing by Herbs

For use in every Home,

BY

Dr. EDWARD BACH.

ADMISSION FREE.

– I –

Wallingford Lecture

[A public lecture on Bach's 50th birthday]

From the earliest times in history we find that herbs have been used as healing remedies, and as far back as records go man has had the faith that in the herbs of the meadow and valley and hillside lay the power to cure his illnesses. Hundreds of years before Christ, the ancient Indians and Arabians and other races were experts in the use of Nature's gifts; also the early Egyptians, and later the Greeks and Romans, and in a lesser degree right on up till our time.

Now it is not likely that for thousands of years, great nations of different creeds and colours should have continuously believed in, and persistently studied and used the herbs of Nature as cures, unless behind it all was a great truth.

In olden days, not only the physicians of the countries used and taught the use of herbs, but the people themselves had great knowledge of their virtue, and were able to care for themselves in many cases of disorders.

This country (England) is no exception, although at the present time the use of natural means is not so general, yet until but a generation or two ago, and even today in the more remote parts of the land, households possessed their own herb chest and cures for their household illnesses.

There have been different books written in England during the last four or five hundred years on Herbal Healing, one of the last and most famous is Kulpepper's, written some nearly three hundred years ago.

This book you can still find, studied and used and highly prized in the more country homes of the British Isles and though it contains the account of over 300 herbs, which must mean much study, yet such is the faith still living that people take the trouble to master it and treat most of their complaints.

During history there have been times when disease was successfully dealt with by practically herbs alone, at other times the great and
natural art of healing has largely been forgotten: this is one of those
times. But such is the power of Nature's way, that it is certain to
return to us.

In olden times when a great nation disappeared, much of its
learning was lost with it, but now, since discoveries are made at once
more universal, there is hope that the blessings bestowed upon us as
they are re-discovered will be spread world-wide, and so always safely
preserved in some country. The herbs spoken of in this lecture,
although but recently discovered, are already being used widely in
very many parts of the world.

It is certain that at those times when the right herbs were known
and used, wonderful healing results must have been general, and the
people of those ages must have had very great faith in them; unless
this were so, the fame, the faith, the belief of cure placed in herbs
would not have survived the rise and fall of empires and been continuously in the minds of people for hundreds and thousands of years.

Healing with the clean pure beautiful agents of Nature is surely the
one method of all which appeals to most of us, and deep down in our
inner self, surely there is something about it that rings true indeed –
something which tells us, this is Nature's way and is right.

To Nature we look confidently for all the needs to keep us alive –
air, light, food, drink and so on: it is not likely that in this great
scheme which provides all, the healing of our illnesses and distress
should be forgotten.

So we see that herbal treatment goes back to the very earliest times
known to man, that it has continued all these centuries both in use and
in fame, and at many times in history has been the chief and almost
the only method of healing.

The system being spoken of this evening has great advantages over
others.

Firstly: All the remedies are made from beautiful flowers,
                plants and trees of Nature, none of them is
                poisonous nor can do any harm, no matter how
                much was taken.

Secondly: They are only 38 in number, which means that it
                is easier to find the right herbs to give than when
                there are very many.

Thirdly: The method of choosing which remedies to give is simple enough for most people to understand.

Fourthly: The cures which have been obtained have been so wonderful that they have passed all expectations of even those who use this method, as well as of the patients who have received the benefit.

These herbs have succeeded again and again where all other treatment which has been tried has failed.

And now, having given you some idea of how ancient and re-nowned is the great Art of Healing the suffering by means of herbs, let us pass on to the main reason of this evening's address.

The main objects of this evening's lecture are two:

Firstly: to describe to you a new method of herbal healing.

Secondly: to reduce as much as possible any fear that any of you may have of disease.

Although it is but comparatively few years ago since the first of a series of the 38 herbs, which are the subject of this address, was discovered, yet in that short time these herbs have been proved to have the most wonderful power of healing. This proof has been found not only in this country, not only in countries on the continent, but in lands as far distant as India, Australia, New Zealand, America and so on.

The important points of treatment with these herbs are:

(1)   that the remedies are all made from beautiful plants and trees of Nature, and that none of them is hurtful nor can they do any harm.

(2)   that without a knowledge of medicine their use can be understood so easily that they can be used in the household.

Think a minute what this means. There are amongst us in almost every town or village some who have to a lesser or greater degree the desire to be able to help in illness; to be able to relieve the suffering and heal the sick, but from circumstances have been prevented from becoming doctors or nurses, and have not felt that they were able to carry out their desire or mission. These herbs place in their hands the power to heal amongst their own families, friends and all around them.

In addition to their occupation, they are enabled in their spare time to do a very great amount of good, as many are so doing today; and there are some who have even given up their work to devote all their time to this form of healing.

It means to those who always had an ideal, a dream of relieving the suffering, that it has been made possible for them, whether it be but their own household or on a wider scale.

Again to impress upon you that there is no need of scientific knowledge necessary when treating with these herbs – not even the name of the illness or disease is required. It is not the disease that matters – it is the patient. It is not what the patient has. It is not the disease, so-called, that really is the important thing to treat, because the same disease may cause different results in different people.

If the effects were always the same in all people, it would be easy to know what the name of the disease was, but this is not so: and this is the reason why often in medical science, it is so difficult to give a name to the particular complaint from which the patient is suffering.

It is not the disease that is of importance, *it is the patient*, the way in which he or she is affected, which is our true guide to healing.

In ordinary life, every one of us has a character of our own. This is made up of our likes, our dislikes, our ideas, thoughts, wishes, ambitions, the way we treat others and so on.

Now, this character is not of the body, it is of the mind, and the mind is the most delicate and sensitive part of ourselves. So can we wonder that the mind with its various moods will be the first to show the symptoms of disease, and being so sensitive, will be a much better guide to us in illness than depending on the body.

Changes in our minds will guide us clearly to the remedy we need, when the body may show little alteration.

Now let us turn our attention to some of the different ways in which one particular complaint can affect an individual.

We all know that the same illness may take us quite differently. If Tommy gets measles, he may be irritable – Sissy may be quiet and drowsy – Johnny wants to be petted – little Peter may be all nerves and fearful – Bobbie wants to be left alone, and so on.

Now if the disease has such different effects, it is certain it is no use treating the disease alone. It is better to treat Tommy, Sissy, Johnny and Peter and Bobby and get them each well, and goodbye the measles.

What it is important to impress upon you, is that it is not the measles which gives the guide to the cure, but it is the way the little one is affected; and the mood of the little one is the most sensitive guide as to know what that particular patient needs.

And just as moods guide us to the treatment in illness so also they may warn us ahead of a complaint approaching and enable us to stop the attack.

Little Tommy comes home from school unusually tired or drowsy or irritable or wanting to be fussed, or perhaps left alone and so on. He is not quite 'himself' as we say. Kind neighbours come in and say "Tommy is sickening for something", you will have to wait! But why wait? If Tommy is treated then according to his mood, he may very soon be turned from not quite himself into himself, when whatever illness was threatened will mostly not occur, or if it does, so slightly as to be hardly noticeable.

And so with any of us, before almost all complaints there is usually a time of not being quite fit, or a bit run down; that is the time to treat our conditions, get fit and stop things going further.

Prevention is better than cure, and these remedies help us in a wonderful way to get well, and to protect ourselves from attack of things unpleasant.

So much for the earliest stages of disease.

Now let us think about those who have been ill for some time, or even a long time. There is again every reason to be hopeful of benefit, either improvement or recovery. Never let anyone give up hope of getting well.

Also do not let anyone be frightened at the name given to any disease; after all, what is in a name; and there is no disease of itself which is incurable. This can be asserted because those suffering from those types of complaints whose names are most dreaded and feared have become well. If some patients have done this, so can others. It takes less time occasionally to cure a so-called terrible illness in some, than one considered less severe in others. It depends more on the individual than the illness.

Now it is just the same principle of treatment in long illnesses as when they are short and slight or only even threatened. Because in a complaint which has been going on for some time, we still have our characters, our wishes, hopes, ideas, likes, dislikes and so on.

So again all that is required is to take notice how a patient is being affected by the illness – if there is depression, hopelessness of getting well, fear of becoming worse, irritability, wanting companionship, desire to be quiet and alone, and so on, and to choose the remedy or remedies suitable for the different moods.

And it is wonderful here again, that just as in threatened illness, if we can get a patient back from being not quite themselves, the disease will not happen. So in cases which have been going on for a long time, as the various moods, depression, fear etc, disappear, so the patients are better in themselves, more like their real selves, and with this, the disease, no matter what it may be, goes also.

There is yet another class of people quite different; those who are not really ill in the ordinary sense of the word, yet are always having something wrong with them; perhaps not serious, yet quite enough to make life a trial and a burden at times, and who would be grateful indeed to be rid of their complaints. Mostly they have tried many things to be free of their trouble, but have not been able to find a cure.

Amongst such are those who have frequent headaches; others are subject to severe colds each year, some suffer from catarrh, or 'rheumatics', or indigestion or eye-strain, or asthma, or slight heart trouble, sleeplessness and so on, whatever it may be.

And what a joy it is to be able to give such people relief; when often they had expected they would have to bear their infirmities all their life; especially to those who had dreaded that their symptoms might get worse with age. Such cases can be cured and very often benefit begins soon after treatment has started.

And lastly, one more class; people who are quite well, strong and healthy and yet have their difficulties.

Such people who find their work or play made more difficult from things like – over-anxiety to do right, or are too enthusiastic and strain and tire themselves; or those who fear failure, imagining themselves not as clever as other people; or those unable to make up their minds as to what they want; those who are afraid something will happen to those dear to them, who always fear the worst, even without any reason; those who are too active and restless and never seem at peace; those who are too sensitive and shy and nervous, and so on. All such things, though they may not be called illnesses, cause unhappiness and worry, yet all these can be put right and an added joy comes into life.

So we see how great is the power of the right herb to heal, not only to keep us strong and protect us from disease, not only to stop an illness when it is threatened, not only to relieve and cure us when we may be in distress and ill, but even to bring peace and happiness and joy to our minds, when there is apparently nothing wrong with our health.

Once again let it be made quite certain that, whether it is being run down, or not quite oneself, whether trying to prevent a disease, whether it is a short illness or a long, the principle is the same, TREAT THE PATIENT; treat the patient according to the mood, according to the character, the individuality, and you can not go wrong.

Think once again the joy this brings to anyone who wants to be able to do something for those who are ill, to be able to help even those where medical science can do no more; it gives to them the power to be healers amongst their fellows.

Yet again, think what a different outlook this brings into our lives, the loss of fear and the increase of hope.

This work of healing has been done and published and given freely so that people like yourselves can help yourselves either in illness or to keep well and strong. It requires no science, only a little knowledge and sympathy and understanding of human nature, which is usual with almost all of us.

THE REMEDIES

There is not time this evening to give you an outline of the whole thirty-eight remedies. And it is not entirely necessary, because if you understand the way in which three or four are used, you have the principle which applies to all.

So we will consider the remedies which are given in case of FEAR. It does not matter whether it is an accident, sudden illness, a long illness or even in those who are quite well in themselves. If fear is present, one of the remedies for fear should be given.

Of course, other remedies may be required at the same time, as there may be other conditions present, then they would be given in addition, but that depends on the case.

Fear is very common in some form or other, not only amongst the ill, but amongst ourselves who otherwise may be well. But whatever it may be, the remedies will help us to be free of that great burden which we call fear.

There are five types of fear, and therefore there are five remedies, one for each type.

The first is when the fear is very great, amounting to terror or panic; either in the patient or because the condition is so serious as to cause intense fear to those around. It may be in the case of sudden illness or accident, but always when there is great emergency or danger, give the remedy for this, made from a small plant which is called Rock Rose.

Rock Rose is a beautiful thing with bright yellow flowers; it grows on hillsides often where the ground is stony or rocky, and a cultivated variety is to be found on rockeries in gardens, though the one growing naturally should always be chosen for healing.

This remedy has had wonderful results and many an alarming case has been better within minutes or hours of its being given.

The key-notes for this remedy are: panic, terror, great emergency or danger.

The second kind of fear is more common: and is the one which applies to everyday life.

The ordinary fears so many of us get: fear of accidents, fear of illness, fear of a complaint getting worse, fear of the dark, of being alone, of burglars, or fire; of poverty, of animals, of other people and so on. Fears of definite things, whether there be any reason or not.

The remedy for this is a beautiful plant called Mimulus; rather like Musk. It grows in the clear running streams and along the banks.

The third kind of fear is of those vague unaccountable things which cannot be explained. As if something dreadful is going to happen, without any idea as to what it may be.

All such dreads for which no reason can be given, and yet are very real and disturbing to the individual require the remedy of the Aspen Tree. And the relief which this has brought to many is truly wonderful.

The fourth kind of fear is that when there is a dread of the mind being over-worked, and the fear that it cannot stand the strain.

When impulses come upon us to do things we should not in the ordinary way think about or for one moment consider.

The remedy for this comes from the Cherry Plum which grows in the hedge-rows of the country-side. This drives away all the wrong ideas and gives the sufferer mental strength and confidence.

Lastly, the fifth kind is the fear for others, especially those dear to us.

If they return late, there is the thought that some accident must have happened; if they go for a holiday, the dread that some calamity will befall them. Some illnesses become very serious complaints, and there is a great anxiety even for those who are not dangerously ill. Always fearing the worst and always anticipating misfortune for them.

The remedy made from the Red Chestnut Blossom of the tree so well known to all of us, soon removes such fears and helps us to think normally.

It is not easy to confuse these five different kinds of fear, as they are quite distinct; and although fear is the commonest mood we have to treat, it requires but one or more of five remedies to combat it in all its forms.

Amongst the other remedies you will find those which will apply to all the conditions that can be met. Such as some for those who suffer from uncertainty, never knowing quite what they wish or what is right for them. Some for loneliness; others for those who are too sensitive. Others for depression, and so on.

And with very little effort it becomes easy to find the remedy or remedies which a patient needs to help them.

Once more, the important point is this: that wonderful as it may seem, relieve your patient of the mood or moods such are given in this system of healing, and your patient is better.

— II —

Masonic Lecture

[Given to a masonic gathering, October 1936]

I come to you tonight with a great message: with a message that may almost be beyond your belief: and yet is is true, and it should bring hope and comfort to very many.

The message is this: THAT DISEASE IS CURABLE.

By the means of the Herbs of which I am speaking tonight, there is no ordinary disease known in this country which has not been cured.

Hundreds of thousands of people who had ailments, who had complaints which they had expected would remain with them the rest of their lives, have been [made] well.

INTRODUCTION

I am not going to attempt this evening to give you any details of the wonderful Herbs which are the subject of this address. All that you can obtain from the book.

The main principles are these:

Firstly:	That no medical knowledge whatever is required.
Secondly:	
	That the disease itself is of no consequence whatsoever.
Thirdly:	That the mind is the most sensitive part of our bodies, and hence the best guide to tell us what remedy is required.
Fourthly:	Thus the manner in which a patient reacts to an illness is alone taken into account. Not the illness itself.
Fifthly:	That such as: fear, depression, doubt, hopelessness, irritability, desire for company or desire to be alone, indecision, such are the true guides to

the way in which a patient is being affected by his
malady, and to the Remedy which he needs.

There is no need to tell you of the Great Healing Properties of these
Remedies, more than to say that hundreds and thousands of people
have been brought back to health who had no hope of anything but
life-long malady. And vast numbers have been quickly cured of
ordinary illness: and again, vast numbers have had disease prevented
in its early stages.

Moreover the fame of these Herbs is such that they are not only
being used in these Islands, but in most of the countries of the world.

The whole principle of Healing by this method is so simple as can
be understood by almost everyone, and even the very Herbs themselves can be gathered and prepared by any who take delight in such.

PART TWO

Brethren, we are taught that within us dwells a Vital and Immortal
Principle.

Man throughout all the centuries of which we have history has
believed that there was something within himself, greater and more
wonderful than his body, and which lived on after the grave.

This belief has been in the mind of man from time immemorial.

We are all conscious that it is not our bodies alone which are the
cause of our difficulties. We do not say, "my body is worried or
anxious or depressed"; we say, "I am worried or anxious or
depressed". We do not say, "my hand hurts itself in pain"; we say,
"my hand hurts me".

Were we but bodies, our lives would be merely one of personal
interest and gain, seeking but our own comforts and relieving our own
needs.

But this is not so. Every kindly smile, every kindly thought and
action; every deed done for love or sympathy or compassion of others
proves that there is something greater within us than that we see.
That we carry a Spark of the Divine, that within us resides a Vital and
Immortal Principle.

And the more that Spark of Divinity shines within us, the more our
lives radiate Its sympathy, Its compassion and Its love, the more we
are beloved by our fellow-men and fingers are pointed at us and the
words are said, "There goes a God-like man".

Moreover, the amount of peace, of happiness, of joy, of health and of well-being that comes into our lives depends also on the amount of which the Divine Spark can enter and illuminate our existence.

From time immemorial, man has looked at two great sources for Healing. To his Maker, and to the Herbs of the field, which his Maker has placed for the relief of those who suffer.

Yet one Truth has mostly been forgotten. That those Herbs of the field placed for Healing, by comforting, by soothing, by relieving our cares, our anxieties, bring us nearer to the Divinity within. And it is that increase of the Divinity within which heals us.

It is a very wonderful thought, but it is absolutely true, that certain Herbs, by bringing us solace, bring us closer to our Divinity: and this is shown again and again in that the sick not only recover from their malady, but in so doing, peace, hope, joy, sympathy and compassion enter into their lives; or if these qualities had been there before, become much increased.

Thus we can truly say that certain Herbs have been placed for us by Divine Means, and the help which they give to us, not only heals our bodies, but brings into our lives, our characters, attributes of our Divinity.

So in healing with these Herbs, the body is not taken into any account; whatever may be wrong with it is of no consideration. All we seek are those characters of the sufferer where he is in disharmony with the Well of Peace in his Soul.

Thus the ordinary symptoms of the flesh are ignored, and all thought is given to such things as depression, impatience, worry, fear, indecision, anxiety, doubt, intolerance, condemnation and so on. All those qualities which are absent in the stillness, the certainty, the compassion of our Inner Selves.

And as by treatment with the Divine Herbs of Healing these adverse qualities will disappear, so with their disappearance, no matter what the disease, the body becomes well.

It is as though in this vast civilisation of today, a civilisation of great stress and strain, the turmoil has been such that we have become too far parted from the true Source of Healing, Our Divinity. Yet our Maker, knowing these things, took compassion upon us, and in His Mercy provided a substitute means to heal our infirmities until when time or circumstance shall restore the genuine and direct.

Yet these substituted means are wonderful in their help: for to see the joy, the happiness, the tenderness that comes into life after life as the Herbs heal them, prove beyond doubt that, not the body alone has received blessing.

Moreover, it is certain that it is increased harmony between the Greater Self within and the body without which has affected the cure.

There is no need to go into detail of the whole 38: that can be obtained from the book. Suffice it to say that there is one for every mood which can be an opposition to our happy joyful selves. And all that is necessary is to know that mood or moods present in the patient and give the Remedy or Remedies which remove them.

It does not matter whether the illness is of only a few minutes or of many years duration, the principle is the same.

Moreover, consider what this means in everyday life. Nearly all of us have some trait which is out of harmony, such as depression, worry, fear and so on. These Herbs remove such and by so doing not only close the door to the entrance of disease, but make our lives happier, more joyous and more useful.

And what greater is there amongst all the Noble Arts than that of Healing. And what more befitting to the Brotherhood of Man than, like some of the Orders of Old, to carry ease to those in pain; solace to those in trial or distress; and comfort and hope to all those afflicted.

And these Remedies place in the hands of everyone the power to do these things. Not of their own power, but of the Power vested by the Great Creator in His Healing Herbs.

— III —

Letters & Miscellaneous Writings

[1933–1936]

Marlow 1933

[*]In the main principle, the fault on earth is the desire for worldly things: a great danger in heaven is the greed and too great desire for spiritual things. And just as on earth greed can so hamper the rising soul, you will find the same in spiritual life, where utter humility and service is needed rather than the desire for perfection.

The desire to be good, the desire to be God, may be as great a hindrance in spiritual life as the desire for gold or power is in earthly experience. The further one advances, the greater must be the humility and the patience and the desire to serve.

In the old path you were fighting the greed for gold (gold is the emblem of worldly power); in the new world, strange as its may seem, you are fighting the greed for good. "Which of us should be greater in the Kingdom of Heaven?"

The hindrance to spiritual advance is the desire to progress.

In this Kingdom it is 'being' no[t] aspiring: the 'being' brings its own reward. This refers not only to this life, but more so to those who seek the spiritual world. There must be no desire to be good, no desire for rapid improvement or perfection, but to be humbly content to wait in any station of service until called to a higher.

In this realm, we do not progress by our own effort, but merely wait until we are considered worthy.

On earth, effort: in Heaven, the reverse.

This means that to make even the greatest sacrifice for the sake of gaining spiritual greatness, even this is wrong. It is like the rich young

*Concerned readers may care to compare this with a version printed in the *Bach Remedy Newsletter* Vol. 5, No. 37; April 1984, p.283. The same piece entitled *Being* was printed again in Vol. 6, No. 6; December 1986, p.42. The original for that form was printed Vol. 3; September 1962, p.23.

man who said "All these things have I done," but it did not open to
him the door of Heaven.

The only way is impersonal service done, not even for spiritual
promotion, but just for the desire to serve. This is the keynote of the
hindrances you are now to investigate.

We are used to training ourselves that our bodies must not count,
that there must be no self; then must be realised that our souls must
not count.

For the next coming of Christ, there is a band of people who, to
welcome Him, should be able to transcend their physical natures and
realise their spirituality.

*

[Letter probably addressed to *The Naturopathic Journal*]

4, Brunswick Terrace,
Cromer,
Norfolk.

October 29, 1933

Dear Folk,

Enclosed what I feel to be two very wonderful papers, they are not
very long but they contain an immense ground work of thought. Miss
Weeks' paper also is very fitting to these three.

If you approve of all we are sending you we are certainly keeping
you stocked well ahead.

I am being cautious as regards astrology, and that is why one left
out the Signs and the months in the first Twelve Healers.[*] This
work is decidedly going to assist vastly in the purification and understanding of astrology, but my part seems to be to give general
principles whereby people like you who have a more detailed
knowledge, may discover a great truth. That is why I do not wish to
be associated with anything dogmatic, until one is sure.

*See below p.77.

The enclosed one knows is right, and hence ready for publication, but the exact placing of Signs and planets and bodily systems, for the moment, has not certainty.

With the very best of wishes to you,

Edward Bach.

Might these three appear in same magazine? merely suggestion.

*

[Letter written from the same address, 9th November 1933]

Dear Folk,

I think Miss Weeks' article is the simplist and most beautiful yet written.[*]

She is a mighty power for good: because childlike she sees things from the simplest pure way.

'Tany rate that's how it strikes me: see what you think.

Our love to you: brave comrades.

*

[Written 13th December 1933 at Cromer, Norfolk]

What we call 'love' is a combination of greed and [fear] that is, desire for more and fearing to lose. Therefore what we call 'love' must be IGNORANCE.

Real love must be infinitely above our ordinary comprehension, something tremendous, the utter forgetfulness of self, the losing of the individuality in the Unity, the absorption of the personality in the Whole.

*Two articles on the Twelve Healers "from a lay point of view" were written by Nora Weeks and published in *Heal Thyself*, (previously *The Homœopathic World*) a monthly magazine edited by J. Ellis Barker; March 1933.

Thus it appears that love is the very opposite of self.

When we understand these terms then we shall we understand the teachings of Christ, they will no longer be parables. Love, in a way, seems to be service combined with wisdom.

What we call 'love' is everyone who gives to us because it satisfies our desire of greed for more, and what we call hate is everyone who takes from us because it stimulates our fear of losing.

When we realise that we have nothing on this earth that is not worth while losing, but everything to gain, then we cannot know hate and then in the proper meaning of the word we shall be able to 'love our enemies'.

Real love of God or our fellows seems to be the desire to serve without reward.

Probably the nearest we ever know to love is for the unattainable, sunsets, starry nights, music, and the beauty of the mountains and moors.

In our heart of hearts we must know that our enemies are those who give way to us, because by so doing they make a bond, a bond we find almost impossible to break and we thank them when they struggle free.

Anyone over whom we can influence our will or control or power is a danger to our freedom. No matter whether our influence is due to love or power or fear or what they get from us. Our souls must thank all those who refuse to be our servants, since it robs them and us our individuality.

*

A Story of the Zodiac
[1934]

When our Lord, the Great Brother of the race, deemed it time for us to learn yet another lesson from the great Book of Life, the messenger came all shining in the darkness of night, in the cold of winter when the physical life is inward drawn, and heralded the new revelation of yet another aspect of Love which man was now growing strong enough to bear. But men were terribly afraid of the Light and the Angels, so that instead of feeling joy and happiness, they had to be told to fear not that Peace and Goodwill would come to them. To these tidings they listened with bended knees, with eyes downcast, to make sure that the safe earth, which they knew, was still beneath their feet, for of this alone they were sure. Now the soil on which they lived and which gave them food in abundance, held many herbs for their healing but these they would have to find for themselves.

The wise Brothers of the race who had long ago received the joyful news from the stars sought for these herbs, these true friends of man, which held powers for their healing and they found the Twelve Healers through virtue of the Four Helpers.

The Four Helpers were the faith in a better world which they hoped one day to attain, now reflected in the flaming Gorse bush. The perseverance of the Oak which braved all tempests, offering shelter and support to the weaker things. The willingness to serve of Heather, which was glad to cover with its simple beauty the arid wind-tossed spaces, and the pure springs gushing from the rocks, bringing brightness and refreshment to those weary and sore after battle.

*

The Story of the Oak Tree
[1934]

One day, and not very long ago, a man was leaning against an oak tree in an old park in Surrey, and he heard what the oak tree was thinking. Now that sounds a very funny thing, but trees do think, you know, and some people can understand what they are thinking.

This old oak tree, and it was a very old oak tree, was saying to itself, "How I envy those cows in the meadow that can walk about the field, and here I am; and everything around so beautiful, so wonderful, the sunshine and the breezes and the rain and yet I am rooted to the spot".

And years afterwards the man found that in the flowers of the oak tree was a great power, the power to heal a lot of sick people, and so he collected the flowers of the oak trees and made them into medicines, and lots and lots of people were healed and made well again.

Some time after this on a hot summer's afternoon, the man was lying on the edge of a corn-field very nearly asleep, and he heard a tree thinking, as some people can hear trees think. The tree was speaking to itself very quietly, and it was saying, "I don't any longer envy the cows who can walk about the meadows, because I can go to all the four quarters of the world to heal the people who are ill": and the man looked up and found that it was an oak tree thinking.

*

The Walnut Tree
[Written 1st January 1935]

This remedy, Walnut, is the remedy of advancing stages: teething, puberty, change of life.

Also for the big decisions made during life, such as change of religion, change of occupation, change of country.

It is the remedy for a great change. The remedy for those who have decided to take a great step forward in life. The decision to step forward, to break old conventions, to leave old limits and restrictions, and to start on a new and better way, often brings with it physical suffering because of the slight regrets, the slight heart-breakings at severance from old ties, old associations, old thoughts.

This remedy will soothe and help to abolish the physical reactions under such conditions, whether the step forward being taken is of a mental or physical nature.

It is the remedy which helps us to pass through all such states without regrets, without memories of the past, without fears for the future, and therefore saves us from the mental and physical suffering which is so often associated with such events.

Undoubtedly a great spell-breaker, both of things of the past commonly called heredity, and circumstances of the present.

*

Let Us Be Ourselves

Has it ever occurred to you that God gave you an individuality? Yet He certainly did. He gave you a personality of your very own, a treasure to be kept to your very own self. He gave you a life to lead, which you and only you should lead: He gave you work to do, which you and only you can do: He placed you in this world, a Divine being, a child of Himself, to learn how to become perfect, to gain all knowledge possible, to grow gentle and kind, and to be a help to others.

And has it ever occurred to you how God speaks to you, and tells you of your own individuality, and of your very own work, of how to steer your ship true to its own course? He speaks to you through your own real desires which are the instincts of your Soul. How else could He speak?

If we but listen to and obey our own desires, uninfluenced by any other personality, we shall always be led aright; we shall always be guided, not only along the path which will lead us to our own advancement and perfection, but also to make our lives to the uttermost useful and helpful to others. It is being influenced by the desires of others that takes us from our own work and wastes our time. Christ would never have fulfilled His Mission had He listened to the persuasion of His parents, and we should have lost an army of world-helpers such as Florence Nightingale and a host of others, had they yielded to the wishes of others and not remained true to their own heart's desires.

What better resolution in the coming of the New Year can we make than to listen to our own desires which are messengers from our Souls, and to have the courage to obey them.

*

[Written at Sotwell 4th August 1935]

No man would be a leader amongst others for any length of time unless he were more expert in his special branch of knowledge than his followers: whether it be army, statesmanship or whatever it may be.

It therefore follows, to be a leader against trouble, difficulties, disease, persecution and so forth, the leader must still have a greater knowledge, a more intimate experience than, pray God, his followers need ever suffer.

*

The Little Black Dog

I wonder if Christ had a little black dog,
    All curly and wooly like mine;
With two long silky ears and a nose, round and wet,
    And two eyes, brown and tender, that shine.

I am sure, if He had, that that little black dog
    Knew right from the first, He was God;
That he needed no proof that Christ was Divine,
    And just worshipped the ground where He trod.

I'm afraid that He hadn't, because I have read
    How He prayed in the garden, alone;
For all of His friends and disciples had fled –
    Even Peter, the one called a stone.

And, oh, I am sure that that little black dog,
    With a heart so tender and warm,
Would never have left Him to suffer alone,
    But, creeping right under His arm,

Would have licked the dear fingers, in agony clasped,
    And, counting all favors, but loss,
When they took Him away, would have trotted behind
    And followed Him quite to the Cross.

*

[Letter written to colleagues in 1935]

> Mount Vernon,
> Sotwell,
> Wallingford,
> Berks.

July 1

Dear Friends,

The prescription of these new remedies is going to be much more simple than at first appeared, because each of them corresponds to one of the Twelve Healers or the Seven Helpers.

For example: supposing a case is definitely Clematis and does fairly well but not a complete cure, give the corresponding new remedy further to help the cure.

Enclosed a list of those already worked out; the rest we shall receive in due time.

There is no doubt that these new remedies act on a different plane to the old. They are more spiritualized and help us to develop that inner great self in all of us which has the power to overcome all fears, all difficulties, all worries, all diseases.

We may know more of this difference later on, but in all of us, whilst there are definite earthly fears of which we are so very conscious, there are also those vague unknown fears which are more frightening than those of material things; and there is no doubt that in all of those of us who strive to do a little good on our journey through the world, those unknown fears are more common.

Edward Bach

*

[Letter to Dr Wheeler, a colleague and well-known homœopath]

Wellsprings,
Sotwell,
Wallingford,
Berks.

September 24, 1935

Dear Brother Doctor Wheeler,

What a splendid case of Aspen. Thank you so much for the report.

The more we use these remedies, both the new nineteen and the old nineteen, the more wonderful the results; and the people who know of them have such faith that they can be cured, no longer come and say "Can you put me right", but just expect it and take it for granted.

Very kindest wishes to you from all of us.

Edward Bach

I have not yet quite thought out the table you sent, but hoping to let you have a reply about this quite shortly.

∗

[Letter to Colleagues]

Wellsprings,
Sotwell,
Wallingford,
Berks.

September 25, 1935

Dear Friends,

If any of us were arranging a picnic for a party next Wednesday, we should all hope for fine weather, and if any of us were responsible for the arrangements, we might go through a few days' fear and anxiety as to whether it would be fine or not. Some of us would have, perhaps, a few days of real unhappiness.

But if we *knew* that next Wednesday was going to be wet or fine, we should either alter the day or make arrangements to suit the conditions, and there would be no anxiety or fear or unhappiness.

And so it must be with all our fears. It is the ignorance that lies behind: and this seems to be our next problem to remove the ignorance and KNOW.

The life-boat men have no fear because they *know* they will safely return, or if, as very rarely happens, they are drowned, they *know* that all is well.

Fear in some way attracts the very thing of which we are afraid. We bring it upon ourselves. To KNOW would save the fear, or in other words to quote, "Ye shall know the TRUTH, and the TRUTH shall make you free".

Our next problem, all of us, is to KNOW; and each of us in our own way, and any one of us, may be the one to find the solution.

The two cases of which some of you know about, prove so strongly how lack of knowledge causes fear.

The one man, terrified to go in a train, always asked the engine-driver if the communication cord was in order, tested the door handles to see if they opened easily, tested emergency doors of motor buses, and suffered much. The moment he realised he was doing all this in the public interest, for the sake of his fellow-passengers, and that he would be the last man to leave any wreck, all the load and dread of travelling went out of his mind, and it was extraordinary how much happier he became.

The other man who studied science for upwards of forty years, had expert knowledge of almost every branch, had been researching to prove everything could be accounted for by a material explanation. He was unhappy, argumentative and miserable because he found missing links in all directions. But the moment he realised that his life's work had been spent to prove behind it all there was a God, his whole life changed; and as a great scientist no one is more capable or more ardent to continue his mission in the right direction.

These two cases illustrate what is happening to so many of us, and it would turn our arduous and difficult lives into lives of joy if we KNEW instead of always fearing.

So we can know that those of us who have fear are doing good work. It is only just we do not realise that our own fear is for the good of others.

The great secret seems to be – to be afraid and not to be afraid of being afraid, until the time comes when we realise that we are right and are doing good.

Certainly, knowledge, truth would remove from our minds all fear, yet it may be part of the Divine Plan that we prove ourselves far greater by battling on, though we are afraid; and it is for mankind to discover the way to see the Light and remove from mankind the burden of fear.

The wonderful remedies that we have, especially MIMULUS for physical fears, and *especially* ASPEN for mental fears, by the marvellous help they give to suffering people, must have been placed for our use by Divine Providence.

In this little centre, our little group, the results of healing by the Herbs are daily proving so wonderful, and we can say *daily*, that we, and it seems it is no exaggeration to say, that hundreds around us, have completely lost all fear of disease. No matter what Greek or Latin or French or English name it carries we KNOW and it has been proved in all around that all fear of illness is disappearing.

This is a step in the right direction.

May the Great Creator of all help us all to further His Work, until all fears, all anxieties are replaced by child-like naturalness and joy of living.

*

[Written at Sotwell 18th July 1935]

In life there are two kinds of pain; bodily pain and thought pain; and of the two thought pain is the more grievous.

There are some people who pass through life without experiencing either form; like the blacksmith of Norfolk who had a toe that was getting twisted and in the way, so one morning in the middle of his work, with others around, he took off his boot, took a hammer and chisel, chopped off his toe, put a red-hot piece of iron against it to stop the bleeding, put back his boot and resumed work.

The same sort of thing in the North country. They require nothing to ease the pain to have their teeth extracted, but will calmly tell you one by one which they require removed. This class of people naturally doesn't come to us.

Then we come to those who suffer physical pain. They are many who have much bodily suffering and little or none of the thought of anguish. For them especially are the Twelve Healers and the Seven Helpers.

Now we come to the third class, those who need our help if possible more than those with bodily pains. Those who have had but perhaps little or even not a day's illness in their lives, and yet they have suffered unthinkable from the pain and the worry and the . . . [incomplete]

*

[Letter to a benefactor]

Dear Friend,

We cannot thank you enough for your most generous gift to the work. It is very rarely that we receive so generous a contribution.

Your help is the equivalent to sending at least 60 doses to the very poor, and may you, from every one who receives a dose, have a great blessing.

You have sent us this help at a time when we were hard pressed, and no words can possibly express our gratitude to you for encouraging us in a difficult hour.

May our kind wishes and the kind wishes of those who receive benefit all go towards helping you.

On behalf of our little band of workers.

*

[Letter to a patient]

November 3, 1935

Dear Mr—,

On your first visit you mentioned the question of fees, and I believe I said wait for the present.

Our principle is this: that as we are using only the Herbs given to us by Divine Providence, and also that the Art of Healing is too sacred to commercialise, that no charge for profit can be made, so that we leave it to the generosity of our patients, upon whom we entirely depend, not only for ourselves, but for the assistance we are able to give others. Even the houses in which we are working at the present time are lent to us by a charitable lady.

Yet we can assure you that we are grateful indeed for the smallest gifts, as it extends our ability to help the very poor, amongst whom we can number hundreds at the present.

*

[Letter to colleagues]

Wellsprings,
Sotwell,
Wallingford,
Berks.

December 26, 1935

Dear Brothers all,

The whole essence of life is to KNOW our Divinity; that we are unconquerable, invincible, and that no hurt can ever stop us in the victory that we are winning in the Name of our Great Master.

And for folk like ourselves who think of others, who wish to serve, who devote so much of our time and of our worldly good to those in need, could there be any other reason that we do this unless we know within ourselves that we are

DIVINE.

Let us take this Truth in both hands and go forward unafraid. Have we ever wanted for a roof or a crust of bread and cheese? Have we ever wanted for far greater luxuries than these?

Let us all walk Ladies and Gentlemen Unafraid; ever bearing in mind one of the last messages given to us by our Master,
      "LO! I AM WITH YOU ALWAYS."

*

[Written May 21st 1936]

All TRUE KNOWLEDGE comes ONLY from WITHIN OURSELVES, in silent communication with our own Soul.

Doctrines and civilisation have robbed us of the Silence, have robbed us of the knowledge that WE KNOW ALL WITHIN OURSELVES.

We have been led to believe that we must be taught by others, and our own Spiritual Selves have become SUBMERGED.

The acorn, carried hundreds of miles from its mother-tree, knows without instruction how to become a perfect Oak. The fish of the sea and rivers lay their spawn and swim away. The same with the frog. The serpent lays its eggs in the sand, and goes on its journey; and yet within the acorn, and the spawn, and the eggs is all the knowledge necessary for the young to become as perfect as their parents.

Young swallows can find their way to their Winter quarters hundreds of miles away, whilst parent birds are still busy with the second brood.

We need so much to come back to the knowledge that WITHIN OURSELVES LIES ALL TRUTH. To remember that we need seek no advice, no teaching but from within.

The Christ taught us that the lilies of the field, though they neither toiled nor spun, were more perfectly arrayed than Solomon in all his glory.

And the Lord Buddha taught us that we were all on the path to our SELF REALISATION once we became rid of the priests and the books.

*

[Written September 1936]

BY THE GRACE OF GOD it has been revealed that it has pleased Him to give unto all who suffer a cure for their adversities.

These cures are to be found amongst certain Healing Herbs and plants and trees of Nature.

Moreover, it has pleased Him to give these Remedies to the people themselves; for such is their simplicity that the people may find and prepare their own medicines and heal themselves and each other of their adversities.

And it is proved that by means of these Divine Herbs, not only are the sick recovered but that added joy and happiness and gentleness and usefulness come into the lives of all who partake of their Healing Virtue.

The need now is for those who have knowledge of these certain Herbs to go and teach all people how they may use them.

*

[Letter to colleagues October 1936]

Dear Folk,

To save you from any trouble, complications, inquests and so on, one has called in the profession. So that everything is in order.

I have been through the hell-fire of the ordeal before, but, my God, this has brought it home.

Their insinuations, muttered words, serious looks, audible whispered sentences, combined with an outward appearance of kindness and friendly feeling, one received the verdict of utter hopelessness.

It took our distinguished brothers two days of collaboration to find the one weak spot where they could hit a stinging blow; but for the faith in God one would lie down and give it up.

But, fellow-workers, it has served its purpose. Let us double and treble (with the perfect confidence that we have), our efforts to spread the news of hope and certainty of cure amongst the sick.

Never before has one felt the awe that can be imparted by what we call 'consultation'; and knowing as we do that the Divine Herbs can heal all, that God is greater than bodily hurt, that until He has given us the Power to know Him, that He has given to us the substitution of His Healing of our infirmities.

Let us discard all convention, all rules, all regulations, and to the utmost of our strength, enter the Crusade, and take up the Mission of bringing hope to the people. Of going out into the world and teaching them that hidden in Nature are the glorious Remedies which are more Powerful than any evil.

Let us forget our limitations, our personalities, our what we think our smallnesses, and let us realize that we have been chosen, picked and special messengers, blessed knights of the highest order, to crash down this work of terror raised by the professional mind, to damn the unfortunate, to dishearten the weak and to crush the fearful.

We know disease is now under human control; it is but a test and can be made well, and until we find a Greater Way, let us blazen the Truth that there is Salvation for the sick and Hope for the dying.

*

[Letter to Victor Bullen]

October 26, 1936

Dear Vic,

I think now you have seen every phase of this Work.

This last episode of Doctor Max Wolf may be welcomed. It is a proof of the value of our Work when material agencies arise to distort it, because the distortion is a far greater weapon than attempted destruction.

Mankind asked for free-will, which God granted him, hence mankind must always have a choice.

As soon as a teacher has given his work to the world, a contorted version of the same must arise.

Such has happened even from the humblest like ourselves, who have dedicated our services to the good of our fellow-men, even to the Highest of all, the Divinity of Christ.

The contortion must be raised for people to be able to choose between the gold and the dross.

Our work is steadfastly to adhere to the simplicity and purity of this method of healing; and when the next edition of the Twelve Healers becomes necessary, we must have a longer introduction, firmly upholding the harmlessness, the simplicity and the miraculous healing powers of the Remedies, which have been shown to us through a greater Source than our own intellects.

I feel now, dear Brother, that as I find it more and more necessary to go into temporary solitude, you have the whole situation in hand and can cope with all matters either connected with patients or connected with the administration of this work of healing, knowing that people like ourselves who have tasted the glory of self-sacrifice, the glory of helping our brothers, once we have been given a jewel of such magnitude, nothing can deviate us from our path of love and duty to displaying its lustre, pure and unadorned to the people of the world.

*

[Letter to colleagues]

Mount Vernon,
Sotwell,
Wallingford,
Berks.

October 26, 1936

Dear Folk,

It would be wonderful to form a little Brotherhood without rank or office, none greater and none less than the other, who devoted themselves to the following principles:

1.   That there has been disclosed unto to us a System of Healing such as has not been known within the memory of men; when, with the simplicity of the Herbal Remedies, we can set forth with the CERTAINTY, the absolute CERTAINTY, of their power to conquer disease.

2.   That we never criticise nor condemn the thoughts, the opinions, the ideas of others; ever remembering that all humanity are God's children, each striving in his own way to find the Glory of his

Father. That we set out on the one hand, as knights of old, to destroy the dragon of fear, knowing that we may never have one discouraging word, but that we can bring HOPE, aye, and most of all, CERTAINTY to those who suffer.

3. That we never get carried away by praise or success that we meet in our Mission, knowing that we are but the messengers of the Great Power.

4. That as more and more we gain the confidence of those around, we proclaim to them we believe that we are divine agents sent to succour them in their need.

5. That as people become well, that the Herbs of the field which are healing them, are the gift of Nature which is the Gift of God; thus bring them back to a belief in the LOVE, the MERCY, and the tender COMPASSION and the ALMIGHTY POWER OF THE MOST HIGH.

*

[Letter to Nora Weeks, Victor Bullen and Mary Tabor]

November 1, 1936

Dear Lovely People,

There are moments such as this when I am expecting a summons to where I know not.

But if that call comes as it may any minute, I do plead with you, you three, to carry on the wonderful Work we have started. A Work that can rob disease of its powers, the Work which can set men free.

What I have attempted to write, should be added to the introduction of the next edition of 'The Twelve Healers'.

*

An Appeal

To my Colleagues of the Medical Profession

After very many years of research, I have found that certain Herbs have the most wonderful healing properties; and that with the aid of these, a large number of cases which by orthodox treatment we could only palliate, are now curable.

Moreover, on-coming disease can be treated and prevented at that stage when people say, "It is not bad enough to send for a doctor".

But when we gain the confidence of those around that disease should be tackled in its very earliest stages, and moreover, when we are able to explain to them that in the most obstinate and chronic cases it is worth while persevering with treatment, our work will be widely extended. Because we shall have that army of people come to us, days, weeks or months before they otherwise would to have their health adjusted; and secondly, the chronic cases still will not only send for us when they wish for relief of pain or discomfort, but will send to us to continue with their cases in the hopes of a cure being obtained.

The Herbs mentioned can be used in conjunction with any orthodox treatment, or added to any prescription, and will hasten and assist the treatment in all types of cases, acute or chronic, to be more successful.

It is a time amongst us when orthodox medicine is not fully coping with a proportion of disease in this country; and it is a time to regain the confidence of the people, and justify our noble Calling.

The Herbs are simple to every student of human nature to understand, and one of their properties is that they help us to prevent the onset of organic disease when the patient is in that functional state which, in either acute or chronic ailments, so often precedes them.

*

— IV —

The Twelve Healers & Other Remedies

[1936 Edition* published C.W. Daniel Co.]

INTRODUCTION

From time immemorial it has been known that Providential Means has placed in Nature the prevention and cure of disease, by means of divinely enriched herbs and plants and trees. The remedies of Nature given in this book have proved that they are blest above others in their work of mercy; and that they have been given the power to heal all types of illness and suffering.

In treating cases with these remedies no notice is taken of the nature of the disease. The individual is treated, and as he becomes well the disease goes, having been cast off by the increase of health.

All know that the same disease may have different effects on different people; it is the effects that need treatment, because they guide to the real cause.

The mind being the most delicate and sensitive part of the body, shows the onset and the course of disease much more definitely than the body, so that the outlook of mind is chosen as the guide as to which remedy or remedies are necessary.

In illness there is a change of mood from that in ordinary life, and those who are observant can notice this change often before, and sometimes long before, the disease appears, and by treatment can prevent the malady ever appearing. When illness has been present for some time, again the mood of the sufferer will guide to the correct remedy.

Take no notice of the disease, think only of the outlook on life of the one in distress.

---

*First published: 1933. New revised edition: 1934. New enlarged edition: 1936.

Thirty-eight different states are simply described: and there should be no difficulty either for oneself, or for another, to find that state or a mixture of states which are present, and so to be able to give the required remedies to effect a cure.

The title, *The Twelve Healers*, has been retained for this book, as it is familiar to many readers.

The relief of suffering was so certain and beneficial, even when there were only twelve remedies, that it was deemed necessary to bring these before the attention of the public at the time, without waiting for the discovery of the remaining twenty-six, which complete the series.

The original twelve are indicated by asterisks.

THE REMEDIES

And the reasons for giving each

THE 38 REMEDIES

are placed under the following
7 HEADINGS

1. FOR FEAR
2. FOR UNCERTAINTY
3. FOR INSUFFICIENT INTEREST IN PRESENT CIRCUMSTANCES
4. FOR LONELINESS
5. FOR THOSE OVER-SENSITIVE TO INFLUENCES AND IDEAS
6. FOR DESPONDENCY OR DESPAIR
7. FOR OVER-CARE FOR WELFARE OF OTHERS

FOR THOSE WHO HAVE FEAR

*ROCK ROSE

The rescue remedy. The remedy of emergency for cases where there even appears no hope. In accident or sudden illness, or when the patient is very frightened or terrified, or if the condition is serious enough to cause great fear to those around. If the patient is not conscious the lips may be moistened with the remedy. Other remedies in addition may also be required, as, for example, if there is unconsciousness, which is a deep, sleepy state, Clematis; if there is torture, Agrimony, and so on.

*MIMULUS

Fear of worldly things, illness, pain, accidents, poverty, of dark, of being alone, of misfortune. The fears of everyday life. These people quietly and secretly bear their dread, they do not freely speak of it to others.

CHERRY PLUM

Fear of the mind being over-strained, of reason giving way, of doing fearful and dreaded things, not wished and known wrong, yet there comes the thought and impulse to do them.

ASPEN

Vague unknown fears, for which there can be given no explanation, no reason.

Yet the patient may be terrified of something terrible going to happen, he knows not what.

These vague unexplainable fears may haunt by night or day.

Sufferers often are afraid to tell their trouble to others.

RED CHESTNUT

For those who find it difficult not to be anxious for other people.

Often they have ceased to worry about themselves, but for those of whom they are fond they may suffer much, frequently anticipating that some unfortunate thing may happen to them.

FOR THOSE WHO SUFFER
UNCERTAINTY

*CERATO

Those who have not sufficient confidence in themselves to make their own decisions.
They constantly seek advice from others, and are often misguided.

*SCLERANTHUS

Those who suffer much from being unable to decide between two things, first one seeming right then the other.
They are usually quiet people, and bear their difficulty alone, as they are not inclined to discuss it with others.

*GENTIAN

Those who are easily discouraged. They may be progressing well in illness, or in the affairs of their daily life, but any small delay or hindrance to progress causes doubt and soon disheartens them.

GORSE

Very great hopelessness, they have given up belief that more can be done for them.
Under persuasion or to please others they may try different treatments, at the same time assuring those around that there is so little hope of relief.

HORNBEAM

For those who feel that they have not sufficient strength, mentally or physically, to carry the burden of life placed upon them; the affairs of every day seem too much for them to accomplish, though they generally succeeded in fulfilling their task.
For those who believe that some part, of mind or body, needs to be strengthened before they can easily fulfil their work.

WILD OAT

Those who have ambitions to do something of prominence in life, who wish to have much experience, and to enjoy all that which is possible for them, to take life to the full.

Their difficulty is to determine what occupation to follow; as although their ambitions are strong, they have no calling which appeals to them above all others.

This may cause delay and dissatisfaction.

NOT SUFFICIENT INTEREST IN PRESENT CIRCUMSTANCES

*CLEMATIS

Those who are dreamy, drowsy, not fully awake, no great interest in life. Quiet people, not really happy in their present circumstances, living more in the future than in the present; living in hopes of happier times, when their ideals may come true. In illness some make little or no effort to get well, and in certain may even look forward to death, in the hope of better times; or maybe, meeting again some beloved one whom they have lost.

HONEYSUCKLE

Those who live much in the past, perhaps a time of great happiness, or memories of a lost friend, or ambitions which have not come true. They do not expect further happiness such as they have had.

WILD ROSE

Those who without apparently sufficient reason become resigned to all that happens, and just glide through life, take it as it is, without any effort to improve things and find some joy. They have surrendered to the struggle of life without complaint.

OLIVE

Those who have suffered much mentally or physically and are so exhausted and weary that they feel they have no more strength to make any effort. Daily life is hard work for them, without pleasure.

WHITE CHESTNUT

For those who cannot prevent thoughts, ideas, arguments which they do not desire from entering their minds. Usually at such times when the interest of the moment is not strong enough to keep the mind full.

Thoughts which worry and will remain, or if for a time thrown out, will return. They seem to circle round and round and cause mental torture.

The presence of such unpleasant thoughts drives out peace and interferes with being able to think only of the work or pleasure of the day.

MUSTARD

Those who are liable to times of gloom, or even despair, as though a cold dark cloud overshadowed them and hid the light and the joy of life. It may not be possible to give any reason or explanation for such attacks.

Under these conditions it is almost impossible to appear happy or cheerful.

CHESTNUT BUD

For those who do not take full advantage of observation and experience, and who take a longer time than others to learn the lessons of daily life.

Whereas one experience would be enough for some, such people find it necessary to have more, sometimes several, before the lesson is learnt.

Therefore, to their regret, they find themselves having to make the same error on different occasions when once would have been enough, or observation of others could have spared them even that one fault.

LONELINESS

*WATER VIOLET

For those who in health or illness like to be alone. Very quiet people, who move about without noise, speak little, and then gently. Very independent, capable and self-reliant. Almost free of the opinions of others. They are aloof, leave people alone and go their own way. Often clever and talented. Their peace and calmness is a blessing to those around them.

*IMPATIENS

Those who are quick in thought and action and who wish all things to be done without hesitation or delay. When ill they are anxious for a hasty recovery.

They find it very difficult to be patient with people who are slow, as they consider it wrong and a waste of time, and they will endeavour to make such people quicker in all ways.

They often prefer to work and think alone, so that they can do everything at their own speed.

HEATHER

Those who are always seeking the companionship of anyone who may be available, as they find it necessary to discuss their own affairs with others, no matter whom it may be. They are very unhappy if they have to be alone for any length of time.

OVER-SENSITIVE TO INFLUENCES AND IDEAS

*AGRIMONY

The jovial, cheerful, humorous people who love peace and are distressed by argument or quarrel, to avoid which they will agree to give up much.

Though generally they have troubles and are tormented and restless and worried in mind or in body, they hide their cares behind their humour and jesting and are considered very good friends to know. They often take alcohol or drugs in excess, to stimulate themselves and help themselves bear their trials with cheerfulness.

*CENTAURY

Kind, quiet, gentle people who are over-anxious to serve others. They overtax their strength in their endeavours.

Their wish so grows upon them that they become more servants than willing helpers. Their good nature leads them to do more than their own share of work, and in so doing they may neglect their own particular mission in life.

WALNUT

For those who have definite ideals and ambitions in life and are fulfilling them, but on rare occasions are tempted to be led away from their own ideas, aims and work by the enthusiasm, convictions or strong opinions of others.

The remedy gives constancy and protection from outside influences.

HOLLY

For those who sometimes are attacked by thoughts of such kind as jealousy, envy, revenge, suspicion.

For the different forms of vexation.

Within themselves they may suffer much, often when there is no real cause for their unhappiness.

FOR DESPONDENCY OR DESPAIR

LARCH

For those who do not consider themselves as good or capable as those around them, who expect failure, who feel that they will never be a success, and so do not venture or make a strong enough attempt to succeed.

PINE

For those who blame themselves. Even when successful they think that they could have done better, and are never content with their efforts or the results. They are hard-working and suffer much from the faults they attach to themselves.

Sometimes if there is any mistake it is due to another, but they will claim responsibility even for that.

ELM

Those who are doing good work, are following the calling of their life and who hope to do something of importance, and this often for the benefit of humanity.

At times there may be periods of depression when they feel that the task they have undertaken is too difficult, and not within the power of a human being.

SWEET CHESTNUT

For those moments which happen to some people when the anguish is so great as to seem to be unbearable.

When the mind or body feels as if it had borne to the uttermost limit of its endurance, and that now it must give way.

When it seems there is nothing but destruction and annihilation left to face.

STAR OF BETHLEHEM

For those in great distress under conditions which for a time produce great unhappiness.

The shock of serious news, the loss of some one dear, the fright following an accident, and such like.

For those who for a time refuse to be consoled this remedy brings comfort.

WILLOW

For those who have suffered adversity or misfortune and find these difficult to accept, without complaint or resentment, as they judge life much by the success which it brings.

They feel that they have not deserved so great a trial, that it was unjust, and they become embittered.

They often take less interest and less activity in those things of life which they had previously enjoyed.

OAK

For those who are struggling and fighting strongly to get well, or in connection with the affairs of their daily life. They will go on trying one thing after another, though their case may seem hopeless.

They will fight on. They are discontented with themselves if illness interferes with their duties or helping others.

They are brave people, fighting against great difficulties, without loss of hope or effort.

CRAB APPLE

This is the remedy of cleansing.

For those who feel as if they had something not quite clean about themselves.

Often it is something of apparently little importance: in others there may be more serious disease which is almost disregarded compared to the one thing on which they concentrate.

In both types they are anxious to be free from the loss of hope or effort.

CRAB APPLE

This is the remedy of cleansing.

For those who feel as if they had something not quite clean about themselves.

Often it is something of apparently little importance: in others there may be more serious disease which is almost disregarded compared to the one thing on which they concentrate.

In both types they are anxious to be free from the one particular thing which is greatest in their minds and which seems so essential to them that it should be cured.

They become despondent if treatment fails.

Being a cleanser, this remedy purifies wounds if the patient has reason to believe that some poison has entered which must be drawn out.

OVER-CARE FOR WELFARE OF OTHERS

*CHICORY

Those are are very mindful of the needs of others; they tend to be over-full of care for children, relatives, friends, always finding something that should be put right. They are continually correcting what they consider wrong, and enjoy doing so. They desire that those for whom they care should be near them.

*VERVAIN

Those with fixed principles and ideas, which they are confident are right, and which they very rarely change.

They have a great wish to convert all around them to their own views of life.

They are strong of will and have much courage when they are convinced of those things that they wish to teach.

In illness they struggle on long after many would have given up their duties.

VINE

Very capable people, certain of their own ability, confident of success.

Being so assured, they think that it would be for the benefit of others if they could be persuaded to do things as they themselves do, or as they are certain is right. Even in illness they will direct their attendants.

They may be of great value in emergency.

BEECH

For those who feel the need to see more good and beauty in all that surrounds them. And, although much appears to be wrong, to have the ability to see the good growing within. So as to be able to be more tolerant, lenient and understanding of the different way each individual and all things are working to their own final perfection.

ROCK WATER

Those who are very strict in their way of living; they deny themselves many of the joys and pleasures of life because they consider it might interfere with their work.

They are hard masters to themselves. They wish to be well and strong and active, and will do anything which they believe will keep them so. They hope to be examples which will appeal to others who may then follow their ideas and be better as a result.

For those unable to prepare their own supplies the remedies can be obtained from the following chemists:

Messrs KEENE & ASHWELL,

57B New Cavendish Street,

London, W1.

Messrs NELSON & Co., LTD,

73 Duke Street,

Grosvenor Square,

London, W1.

The chemists mentioned have very kindly undertaken to supply these remedies at a very moderate price.

Stock bottles of:

	s.	d.	
One remedy............................		8	(postage 2d.)
Twelve remedies......................	5	0	(postage 4d.)
The complete set of 38	15	6	(postage 6d.)

METHODS OF DOSAGE

As all these remedies are pure and harmless, there is no fear of giving too much or too often, though only the smallest quantities are necessary to act as a dose. Nor can any remedy do harm should it prove not to be the one actually needed for the case.

To prepare, take about two drops from the stock bottle into a small bottle nearly filled with water; if this is required to keep for some time a little brandy may be added as a preservative.

This bottle is used for giving doses, and but a few drops of this, taken in a little water, milk, or any way convenient, is all that is necessary.

In urgent cases the doses may be given every few minutes, until there is improvement; in severe cases about half-hourly; and in long-standing cases every two or three hours, or more often or less as the patient feels the need.

In those unconscious, moisten the lips frequently.

Whenever there is pain, stiffness, inflammation, or any local trouble, in addition a lotion should be applied. Take a few drops from the medicine bottle in a bowl of water and in this soak a piece of cloth and cover the affected part; this can be kept moist from time to time, as necessary.

Sponging or bathing in water with a few drops of the remedies added may at times be useful.

METHOD OF PREPARATION
Two methods are used to prepare these remedies.

SUNSHINE METHOD

A thin glass bowl is taken and almost filled with the purest water obtainable, if possible from a spring nearby.

The blooms of the plant are picked and immediately floated on the surface of the water, so as to cover it, and then left in the bright sunshine for three or four hours, or less time if the blooms begin to show signs of fading. The blossoms are then carefully lifted out and the water poured into bottles so as to half fill them. The bottles are then filled up with brandy to preserve the remedy. These bottles are stock, and are not used direct for giving doses. A few drops are taken from these to another bottle, from which the patient is treated, so that the stocks contain a large supply. The supplies from the chemists should be used in the same way.

The following remedies were prepared as above:

Agrimony, Centaury, Cerato, Chicory, Clematis, Gentian, Gorse, Heather, Impatiens, Mimulus, Oak, Olive, Rock Rose, Rock Water, Scleranthus, the Wild Oat, Vervain, Vine, Water Violet, White Chestnut Blossom.

Rock Water. It has long been known that certain wells and spring waters have had the power to heal some people, and such wells or springs have become renowned for this property. Any well or any spring which has been known to have had healing power and which is still left free in its natural state, unhampered by the shrines of man, may be used.

THE BOILING METHOD

The remaining remedies were prepared by boiling as follows:

The specimens, as about to be described, were boiled for half an hour in clean pure water.

The fluid strained off, poured into bottles until half filled, and then, when cold, brandy added as before to fill up and preserve.

Chestnut Bud. For this remedy the buds are gathered from the White Chestnut tree, just before bursting into leaf.

In others the blossom should be used together with small pieces of stem or stalk and, when present, young fresh leaves.

All the remedies given can be found growing naturally in the British Isles, except Vine, Olive, Cerato, although some are true natives of other countries along middle and southern Europe to northern India and Tibet.

The English and botanical name of each remedy is as follows:

*AGRIMONY	*Agrimonia Eupatoria*
ASPEN	*Populus Tremula*
BEECH	*Fagus Sylvatica*
*CENTAURY	*Erythrœa Centaurium*
*CERATO	*Ceratostigma Willmottiana*
CHERRY PLUM	*Prunus Cerasifera*
CHESTNUT BUD	*Æsculus Hippocastanum*
*CHICORY	*Cichorium Intybus*
*CLEMATIS	*Clematis Vitalba*
CRAB APPLE	*Pyrus Malus*
ELM	*Ulmus Campestris*
*GENTIAN	*Gentiana Amarella*
GORSE	*Ulex Europœus*
HEATHER	*Calluna Vulgaris*
HOLLY	*Ilex Aquifolium*
HONEYSUCKLE	*Lonicera Caprifolium*
HORNBEAM	*Carpinus Betulus*
*IMPATIENS	*Impatiens Royalei*
LARCH	*Larix Europea*
*MIMULUS	*Mimulus Luteus*
MUSTARD	*Sinapsis Arvensis*
OAK	*Quercus Pedunculata*
OLIVE	*Olea Europœa*

PINE..	*Pinus Sylvestris*
RED CHESTNUT	*Æsculus Carnea*
*ROCK ROSE	*Helianthemum Vulgare*
ROCK WATER........................	
*SCLERANTHUS	*Scleranthus Annuus*
STAR OF BETHLEHEM	*Ornithogalum Umbellatum*
SWEET CHESTNUT	*Castanea Vulgaris*
*VERVAIN	*Verbena Officinalis*
VINE	*Vitis Vinifera*
WALNUT.............................	*Juglans Regia*
*WATER VIOLET....................	*Hottonia Palustris*
WHITE CHESTNUT.................	*Æsculus Hippocastanum*
WILD OAT	*Bromus Asper†*
WILD ROSE..........................	*Rosa Canina*
WILLOW..............................	*Salix Vitellina*

And may we ever have joy and gratitude in our hearts that the Great Creator of all things, in His Love for us, has placed the herbs in the fields for our healing.

†There is no English name for Bromus Asper. Bromus is an ancient word meaning Oat.

– V –

The Twelve Healers & Seven Helpers

[Published* C.W. Daniel Co. 1934]

As has been known through all time, the cure of disease lies in the healing herbs of the field; so to all who are ill, know this: that disease could never have gained the power it has today if man had not deserted the natural protection against illness, namely the healing herbs. Moreover, that in those who really desire to get well there is no disease which can resist the power of the antidote to be found in the right plant, and sickness has no more power to persist in the presence of the right herb than darkness can remain in a room when the windows are thrown open to the sunlight.

Though, by forgetting Nature's cure, we have paid heavily with the vast amount of disease today, yet Nature patiently waits, and we have only to turn back to her to find relief from our suffering.

It is only because we have forsaken Nature's way for man's way that we have suffered, and we have only to return to be released from our trials. In the presence of the way of Nature disease has no power; all fear, all depression, all hopelessness can be set aside. There is no disease of itself which is incurable.

This book describes nineteen herbs, which, by Divine Providence, have been enriched with healing powers, so that in those who earnestly desire to be made well, no disease is beyond hope of recovery. Twelve of these herbs are for illness which is beginning or has only lasted a short time, and they are called the Twelve Healers; and seven herbs to help those who have been ill for many weeks or months, or even years, and they are called the Seven Helpers.

We all know that in illness we have different moods from our usual self, and these moods are the guide to us as to the remedy we require. This is valuable because many a disease can be prevented if we rightly

*First published: 1933. New and revised edition: 1934.

interpret those signs which are the warnings of illness. Moreover, people who have been sick for a long or even a very long time can be brought back to health if the right herbs are given, and this again we can know from the mood or state they are in during their suffering.

We all know that pain, for instance, has a different effect upon different people: some are frightened, some depressed, some bad-tempered, some want to be left alone, some wish to be petted, others are bright and cheerful in spite of their suffering; and it is this mood that tells us the remedy they need for true healing, not the mere fact that they are in pain.

If we treat the mood and not the disease we are treating the real person, and we are giving the patient what is truly required to bring back health.

In ordinary everyday life these remedies are also useful for the little ailments such as tiredness, headaches, worry, depression, irritability and so on, because these are warnings and if we drive them away and treat these small troubles, we are keeping ourselves in a really good state of health and protecting ourselves from disease; for we know, sometimes for perhaps many months before a bad illness, people are not really well, and if they could only be treated at that time it might save all the suffering in front of them.

Again, every mother knows that a child may come home from school not his real self, and she says, "he is not well, he is sickening for something." How much better to treat this at once, so that by next morning the child is well and strong, instead of waiting for a day or two to see what will develop.

Everyone who watches will soon realise that a change of mood is present in all who are not well, and if the right remedy is given according to the change, the illness will be shortened and the patient brought back to health.

It does not matter what the disease is, the mood alone has to be treated.

There are only twelve different moods and there is a herb for each, so that it is not difficult to decide which remedy is required.

THE TWELVE HEALERS

Now follow the names of the twelve Healers and the mood belonging to each.

ROCK ROSE

When a patient is terrified, or if the illness is sudden or so serious as to cause great fear to those around. In fact, in all cases of urgency or danger give this remedy, even if others are needed as well.

MIMULUS

When the patient is calm, but quietly afraid.

AGRIMONY

In those who, although they are ill, are bright and cheerful and try to make light of their trouble.

SCLERANTHUS

For those who find it difficult to decide what they want and to make up their minds what they would like. They try first one thing and then another. They feel they want two or three things at the same time, but cannot decide which.

CLEMATIS

When the patient is sleepy or drowsy or dreamy; taking no interest in things; seems far away.

GENTIAN

When there is depression; when they feel that things are not going right, or doubt about their getting well.

CHICORY

In those who are worrying over details, fussing about things, or for those who want much attention or require to be petted.

CENTAURY

For the weak, languid, weary, who have no energy. Quiet and often timid and shy.

CERATO

For those who do not seem to have any absorbing interest in life; who have not much trust in themselves nor self-confidence. Always asking advice from different people but not following it, never feeling quite satisfied that they have the answer they require. Often wish to do things that seem foolish.

VERVAIN

For the obstinate, strong-willed. Do not like advice. Difficult to help. Who, when not well, often keep on long after others would have given in.

IMPATIENS

For the irritable, cross, peevish, impatient.

WATER VIOLET

For those who want to be left alone, perhaps go away and be quiet.

*

Sometimes more than one remedy is needed, as more than one mood may be present. A person may be irritable and depressed, in which case give both remedies, or even if three or four remedies seem necessary, each one should be given, and they can be mixed together. Also during an illness the mood may change from time to time, but always give the remedy that fits the mood at the moment. The change of moods is often a sign of recovery. We all know that after a long illness, no matter what it may have been, we are glad to see the patient becoming impatient, we say they must be better.

There is no danger whatever of any harm being done by these remedies; they all come from beautiful pure herbs which can hurt no one and can only do good.

How to put up the medicine and give the doses is described under directions at the end of the book.

THE SEVEN HELPERS

Next let us consider illness which has been going on for a long time.

If the patient does not improve when what seems the right one of the Healers has been given, there are seven more remedies to prepare the way; because, when an illness is old, it has become more established and may require help before it responds easily, so that the seven remedies for such cases are called the Seven Helpers.

Therefore, if a case has not improved with what is considered the right one of the Healers, give treatment with one of the Helpers.

The first thing to notice is whether the patient is pale or high-coloured.

If pale, either OLIVE, GORSE, or OAK will be needed. If high-coloured, VINE, HEATHER or ROCK-WATER.

The seventh Helper, the WILD OAT, may be required by anyone, and if what seems to be the right one of the Healers or the right one of the other six Helpers does not give benefit, in all such cases try the remedy the WILD OAT.

If the patient is pale, there are three Helpers

OLIVE

For those who are pale, worn-out and exhausted, perhaps after much worry, illness, grief, or some long struggle. In every way they are very tired and feel as if they had no more strength to fight on, and at times hardly know how to keep going. They may depend very much upon others for help.

In some, the skin is very dry and may be wrinkled.

GORSE

For people who feel that their case is hopeless; that they have tried everything and nothing more can be done. They are resigned to their illness and are making no effort.

They generally have rather yellowish complexions, and often dark lines below the eyes.

OAK

For those who are struggling very hard; who are fighting to get well. They are cross with themselves at being ill, because it stops their doing their share of work, and although they feel there is not very much hope of their getting really well, they will try everything in their power to regain their health and usefulness.

For those who are high-coloured

VINE

Those who are very particular. They are so sure that they know right, both for themselves and for others, how things should be done that it makes them critical and exacting. They wish for everything just in their own way, and give orders to those helping them. Even then they are difficult to satisfy.

HEATHER

The big, robust, well-made people, jovial and hearty. They are much concerned with all the details of their maladies and feel that every small item is of much importance. Generally they have not had much illness, and even a little complaint to them seems serious.

ROCK WATER

Those who are very strict with themselves. They will give up everything, however much they may like it, if they think it bad for them, and suffer anything if they think it is good. They have much courage, and will face any treatment if they consider it will help.

They are hard masters, not of others, but to themselves, and so lose much of the joy in life.

THE WILD OAT

Is a remedy that may be needed by anyone, and in cases which do not respond to other herbs, or when it seems difficult to decide which to give, try this for at least a week.

If the patient does well, continue with it so long as they improve before changing to another remedy.

*

In this age, in saying these herbs can cure all disease, it is necessary to add in those who really desire to get well, because under present

conditions illness often brings advantages to a patient which sometimes they do not truly desire to lose. It may bring sympathy or
attention, or save them from work, or be a means of escaping some
duty they wish to avoid, or bring financial gain such as pensions,
compensation and so on. In certain cases it is understandable that
there are those who may be tempted to hold on to a disability or a
malady rather than lose the advantage it brings.

DIRECTIONS

DIRECTION FOR USING THE REMEDIES

To use the remedies, take about a cupful of water and add only three
or four drops from the little bottles supplied by the chemist of the
needful herb or herbs, and stir it up. If it gets stale, throw it away and
mix more, or if it is desired to keep it for some time add two
teaspoonsful of brandy. It does not matter about being exact, as none
of these remedies could do the least harm, even if taken in large
quantities, but as a little is enough, to make up a small amount saves
waste.

For children, give an egg-spoonful, and for grown-ups a
teaspoonful at a time. In very desperate cases doses may be given
every quarter of an hour; in severe cases every hour, and in
ordinary long-standing illness about every two or three hours
spread over the day, or more often if the patient feels it is helping
to take it frequently. As the case gets better, the doses will not be
required to be given so often.

If the patient is unconscious, it is sufficient to moisten the lips with
the remedy, and if in this case the patient is pale, give Rock Rose and
Clematis, or if high-coloured, Rock Rose and Vine.

In illness which is threatened or not long started, even if there is no
improvement, give the remedy chosen about six or seven hours before
trying another one; but in cases of long-standing disease, try a herb
for at least four or five days. If a patient is definitely improving, keep
on with the same remedy so long as he progresses.

For those who want to prepare their own stock remedies, the
method is given below and, following, the English and botanical
names of the plants and the situations where they may be found.

METHOD OF PREPARATION

The remedies should be prepared near the place where the plant grows as the flowers should be used immediately after gathering.

A thin glass bowl is taken, filled with clear water, preferably from a pure spring or stream. Sufficient blooms of the plant are floated on the water to cover the surface, as much as can be done without overlapping the blossoms; then allowed to stand in bright sunshine until the blooms show signs of fading.

The time varies from about two to seven hours according to the plant and the strength of the sun. The blossoms are then gently lifted out.

Bottles are taken and half filled with water from the bowl. The other halves of the bottles are then filled up with brandy to preserve the remedy. These are the stock bottles which will keep for any length of time, and may be used in the same way as the bottles of the remedies supplied by the chemists.

The English and botanical name of each remedy is as follows:-

ROCK ROSE	*Helianthemum Vulgare*
MIMULUS	*Mimulus Luteus*
AGRIMONY	*Agrimonia Eupatoria*
SCLERANTHUS	*Scleranthus Annuus*
CLEMATIS	*Clematis Vitalba*
GENTIAN	*Gentiana Amarella*
CHICORY	*Cichorium Intybus*
CENTAURY	*Erythraea Centaurium*
CERATO	*Ceratostigma Willmottiana*
VERVAIN	*Verbena Officinalis*
IMPATIENS	*Impatiens Royali*
WATER VIOLET	*Hottonia Palustris*
OLIVE	*Olea Europaea*
GORSE	*Ulex Europaeus*
OAK	*Quercus Pedunculata*
VINE	*Vitis Vinifera*
HEATHER	*Calluna Vulgaris*
ROCK WATER	
THE WILD OAT	*Bromus Asper*

These plants are in flower mostly during the months of July, August and September with the exception of those mentioned below:-

APRIL .... *Gorse*
MAY .... *Olive, Vine and Oak*
JUNE .... *Water Violet and the Wild Oat*

The following will give an idea of the places where they may be found, and some counties have local botanical books which will be a clear guide for particular districts, as these books often give exact localities:

ROCK ROSE and GENTIAN, hilly pastures.

MIMULUS is comparatively rare, but grows on the edges of marshes and streams where the water is clear.

AGRIMONY grows throughout the country in hedge-banks and meadows.

CLEMATIS adorns our hedges in many parts of the country where there is chalk.

CHICORY, cornfields and cultivated ground. In some parts it is grown by farmers.

CENTAURY grows in the fields, hedge-banks and meadow-land.

CERATO is at present very rare in this country.

VERVAIN grows by roadsides and in hedge-banks.

IMPATIENS is not a native of this country, but grows to perfection along the banks of some of the Welsh rivers. The colour of the blossoms of this plant varies and only the beautiful pale mauve ones should be chosen.

WATER VIOLET is comparatively rare, but it is to be found in some of our slowly-moving crystal brooks and streams.

OLIVE, Italy and other countries.

GORSE is well known to everyone. The blooms of the Gorse should be taken just before the plant reaches its full glory, a little before it gives out scent.

OAK. The small slender flower-stems of the Oak should be gathered in full bloom.

VINE, Italy, Switzerland and other countries.

HEATHER. The Heather to choose is not the red bell-heather, but the beautiful slender small rose-pink variety such as grows on the Welsh or Scottish mountains.

ROCK WATER. It has long been known that certain well- and spring-waters have had the power to heal some people, and such wells or springs have become renowned for this property. Any well or any spring which has been known to have had healing power and which is still left free in its natural state, unhampered by the shrines of man, may be used. This remedy does not require long exposure to sunshine, about one hour being sufficient.

THE WILD OAT, hedge-banks and woods.

So that in this system of healing, everything may be done by the people themselves, even, if they like, to the finding of the plants and the making of the remedies.

If you look around and study people, you will find that everyone who is ill comes under one or more of the types mentioned, so that the remedy to suit their case can be given.

And it is impossible to count the number of people who have been saved from short illness, and the number who have been cured of disease which has been going on for a long time, and often for a very long time, by these wonderful, natural, divinely enriched herbs of the mountains, and the meadow-lands and the valleys.

And may we ever have joy and gratitude in our hearts that the Great Creator of all things, in His Love for us, has placed the herbs in the fields for our healing.

— VI —

The Twelve Healers & Four Helpers

[Published C.W. Daniel Co. 1933]

THE TWELVE HEALERS*

To all who are ill, know this: that disease could never have gained the power it has today if man had not deserted the natural protection against illness, namely the healing herbs of the field. Moreover, that in those who really desire to be well there is no disease which can resist the power of the antidote to be found in the right plant, and sickness has no more power to persist in the presence of the right herb than darkness can remain in a room when the windows are thrown open to the sunlight.

Though, by forgetting Nature's cures, we have paid heavily with the vast amount of disease today, yet Nature patiently waits and we have only to turn back to her to find relief from our suffering.

From time immemorial mankind has known that the herbs of the field could heal his infirmities, and throughout the ages the names of those who have had the true knowledge of healing with herbs are still remembered by us.

It is only because we have forsaken Nature's way for man's way that we have suffered, and we have only to return to be released from our trials. In the presence of the way of Nature disease has no power; all fear, all depression, all hopelessness can be set aside. There is no disease of itself which is incurable.

In this book is given the description of twelve herbs that have the power to cure all types of disease.

---

*The first section of this, *The Twelve Healers*, was first printed earlier in the same year when Bach was staying in Marlow. He paid for the printing himself. The text is identical to that used here in this edition published by C.W. Daniel Co.

Being herbs of Nature they treat our natures. It is of no consequence whether it be our hand or foot or head or any other part of our body that is diseased, and it is of no consequence whatever from what kind of disease we suffer. It is because there is something wrong in our nature that disease is able to attack us, and it is this something wrong which the herbs put right, and thus not only heal our bodies, but make us healthier and happier in every way and bring joy into our lives.

Thus to find the herb we need, we must not think for one moment of the disease from which we suffer, or whether it is severe or slight, or whether it has been with us but a few hours or for many years. All we have to do is to find what is wrong with our nature and to take the herb which corresponds to this.

Now whatever is wrong shows itself in one or more of twelve definite states, and according to the state present we can judge the remedy we need.

It is not possible for us to be ill unless we are not in harmony with our true nature. But whatever condition is behind our trouble, whatever fault there is in our nature it matters not, because these remedies will help us to correct that fault and thus curing the root-cause of our illness give back to us bodily and mental health.

These remedies bring about a harmonious state of our whole being and often a joy of life, a freedom from cares and anxieties which has not been previously known.

As already stated the faults in our nature are expressed to us by twelve different states, for each of which there is a corresponding herb to bring us back to health.

In brief the twelve states are as follows:

WEAKNESS
DESPAIR
FEAR
TORTURE
INDECISION
INDIFFERENCE
FUSSINESS
SELF-DISTRUST
DISCOURAGEMENT
ENTHUSIASM
IMPATIENCE
ALOOFNESS

Now follows a somewhat fuller explanation of these states together with the name of the remedy for each.

CENTAURY

WEAKNESS

To give strength. The weakness after illness: pale, languid, tired, no energy, limp, exhausted. Drained of vitality. Those who desire peace at any price. Even in illness they may be too willing to help others and get tired and worn-out by their efforts. The mind is often alert, but the body weak, too weak to make much effort. Meek, submissive and imposed upon because of their good natures.

ROCK ROSE

DESPAIR

This is the rescue remedy. In cases of urgency and danger. Whenever things are desperate. In all cases of danger of life. When the patient is terrified or in a panic. In cases when all hope is lost. When there is danger to the mind, of threatened suicide or insanity, or nervous breakdown, fear of death or hopeless depression.

MIMULUS

FEAR

To combat all fear. Fear of disease, of accidents, of unknown things. Fear of people, of relatives, of strangers, of crowds, of noise, of talking or of being questioned, of being alone. Fear of damp, of cold, of heat, of the dark. Fear of complications in illness, or of being incurable.

AGRIMONY

TORTURE

To soothe all those tormented in body or mind and bring them peace. The restless, the worried, the anxious, the tortured. Those who can find no peace of mind, no rest. There is such a vast army of these sufferers who so often hide their torment under smiles and joviality. They are often the cheeriest of people and are frequently humorists.

A great number of these seek refuge in alcohol or even drugs as stimulants to help them to keep going. They will do anything rather than depress others with their trials. Even in severe illness they will jest and make light of their trials. They are brave people and Agrimony will help them so much.

SCLERANTHUS

INDECISION

Those who are unable to make up their minds as to what they want, first one thing seems right and then another. Their wishes, like their bodily symptoms, seem to come and go. If they have temperatures these swing up and down. They are undetermined and unable to decide quickly or definitely, and their decisions quickly change. Uncertainty of bodily actions, giddiness, shaking, jerky uncontrolled movements, unsteady walking. Their moods change quickly, first cheery then depressed. Their conversation may rapidly jump from one subject to another.

CLEMATIS

INDIFFERENCE

To combat all sleepy, drowsy, listless states. When the patient loses interest. Makes no effort to get well. Seems indifferent as to what happens: has no enthusiasm about anything. Only half hear what is said to them. These people are often dreamy, far-away, apathetic, live in their thoughts; maybe thinking too much of someone they have lost, or dream of ambitions they do not strive to realise. The seem contented, being not fully awake, and happy in their dreams of ideals. They are generally quiet and gentle, but they do not find enough joy in life itself; do not live enough in the present. Ordinary fainting may be of this type and in unconscious cases it is sufficient to moisten the lips with the remedy.

CHICORY

FUSSINESS

When ill, these people worry over others, children, friends, relatives; are anxious that they are too warm, too cold, not happy, not enjoying themselves. Constantly asking them how they are and what they would like. Over-anxious in efforts to please them. Many questions as to their wishes and requirements. This state brings no peace and strains the patient. Sometimes the patients feel sorry for themselves; feel that they have done nothing to deserve to be ill; they are ill-used and neglected, that others are not caring for them. Often they have a good colour when ill; the people whose looks do not pity them.

CERATO

SELF-DISTRUST

People who are too easily influenced. For those who have no confidence in themselves, depend too much upon the advice of others and listen first to one and then to another. Their own lack of self-esteem makes them admire and trust too much any who hold strong views; they can easily be led into difficulties on this account. In illness they are quite sure one thing will cure them until they hear of another, and they rush from one trial to the next according to the latest advice. They will do almost anything good or bad for them if the argument is forcible enough. They do not trust their own good judgement. Instead of having their own wishes and desires they will so often quote what others have advised or thought. The ideas and opinions of others are too important to them and this robs them of their own personality. They will always have some excuse for all they do.

GENTIAN

DISCOURAGEMENT

For those who are faltering or are despondent. Look on the dark side and are pessimistic. In convalescence when they think they have come to a standstill; really doing well but tend to be discouraged and doubt that they are making progress. This is for those who feel as if the difficulties before them are too big to be overcome and temporarily lose heart. In this state they only want a little encouragement which this remedy will give them and they will do well.

VERVAIN

ENTHUSIASM

The strong-willed. Those who are intense of mind, who tend to over-exert themselves mentally and physically. They refuse to be beaten and will carry on long after others would have given in. They go their own way. They have fixed ideas and are very certain that they know right. They may be obstinate in refusing treatment until compelled. They may be carried away by their enthusiasm and cause themselves much strain. In all things tend to be too serious and tense. Life is a very arduous thing for them. They have their own strong views and sometimes wish to bring others to their point of view and are intolerant of the opinions of others. They do not like to listen to advice. They are often people with big ideals and ambitions for the good of humanity.

IMPATIENS

IMPATIENCE

At all times when there is impatience. Impatient with themselves, wanting to hurry things, wanting to do things quickly, wanting to get well at once, to be out and about again. Impatient with others, irritable over little things, difficult to keep their temper. Cannot wait. This state is common and often a good sign during convalescence, and the restfulness this remedy brings hastens recovery. There is often impatience in severe pain and so Impatiens is of great value at those times to relieve the pain and calm the patient.

WATER-VIOLET

ALOOFNESS

These are very beautiful people in mind and often in body. They are gentle, quiet, very refined and cultured and yet are masters of their fate and lead their lives with a quiet determination and certainty. Like to be much alone. In illness they may be a little proud and aloof and if so this reacts upon them. Even so, they are very brave and try to fight alone and unaided and be of no anxiety or trouble to those around. They are brave souls indeed who seem to know their work in life and do it with a quiet certain will. They do not often form strong attachments even to those nearest them. They bear adversity and illness calmly, quietly and bravely without complaint.

To Prepare the Stock Remedies

The remedies should be prepared near the place where the plant grows as the flowers should be used immediately after gathering. A thin glass bowl is taken, filled with clear water, preferably from a pure spring or stream. Sufficient blooms of the plant are floated on the water to cover the surface, as much as can be done without over-lapping the blossoms; then allowed to stand in bright sunshine until the blooms show signs of fading. The time varies from about two to seven hours according to the plant and the strength of the sun. The blossoms are then gently lifted out and the water poured into bottles with an equal quantity of brandy added as a preservative. These bottles are our stock solutions of the remedies.

Method of Dosage

To Prepare the Doses

When doses are required for a patient, take an ordinary four-ounce medicine bottle, pour into this four drops from the stock bottle of the required remedy, fill up with water and shake well.

This is the medicine which is given to the patient in doses of a teaspoonful as necessary.

Bottles of the remedy supplied by the chemist are stock and are to be used for medicating four-ounce bottles as described here.

To Give the Doses

In very urgent cases doses may be given quite often, as frequently as every quarter of an hour.

If the patient is unconscious it is sufficient merely to moisten the lips with the remedy.

In serious cases doses may be required hourly.

In ordinary cases where the patient has chronic complaint the rule to follow is to give a dose whenever the patient feels the need, whether this be eight or ten times a day or only once or twice.

There is no possible danger of giving over-doses or wrong remedies. None of these beautiful herbs can do any harm, it is simply that if the one the patient needs is administered benefit will result.

If in doubt between one or two, give both; they can be put into the same bottle. This also applies if the patient has two definite states present at the same time, such as fear and impatience.

During an illness more than one state may be present, or one may follow another, then each stage should be treated as it occurs. In severe illness, there may be despair or fear; on recovery, indifference or discouragement; during convalescence, impatience or weakness; and so on. In such cases each stage can be dealt with until it disappears and perfect health is regained.

Everyone who is ill comes under one or more of these twelve states and the remedies to be healed.

After very little study it will be found that it becomes simple to know to which state a patient belongs and the remedy required.

Then comes the realisation of how much more important and how much more helpful this is than thinking only of the bodily affliction. No longer are we concerned with a pain in the head or arm, or a swelling here or a tumour there, but with a state which can be treated and the real cause removed, because these states indicate our trouble and guide us to the herbs which can give us back health and a joy of life.

The botanical name of each remedy is as follows:

CENTAURY	*Erythræa Centaurium*
ROCK ROSE	*Helianthemum Vulgare*
MIMULUS	*Mimulus Luteus*
AGRIMONY	*Agrimonia Eupatoria*
SCLERANTHUS	*Scleranthus Annuus*
CLEMATIS	*Clematis Vitalba*
CHICORY	*Cichorium Intybus*
CERATO	*Ceratostigma Willmottiana*
GENTIAN	*Gentiana Amarella*
VERVAIN	*Verbena Officinalis*
IMPATIENS	*Impatiens Royalei*
WATER VIOLET	*Hottonia Palustris*

These plants are in flower mostly during the months of July, August and September. Water Violet is a little earlier, being at its prime in June and July.

The following will give an idea of the places where they may be found, and some counties have local botanical books which will be a clear guide for particular districts, as these books often give exact localities.

CENTAURY grows in the fields, hedge-banks and meadow-land.

ROCK ROSE, upland pastures.

MIMULUS is comparatively rare, but grows on the edges of marshes and streams where the water is clear.

AGRIMONY grows throughout the country in hedge-banks and meadows.

SCLERANTHUS can be found amongst and around the edges of some cornfields.

CLEMATIS adorns our hedges in many parts of the country where there is chalk.

CHICORY, cornfields and cultivated ground. In some parts it is grown by farmers.

CERATO is not a native of this country and is only to be found on one or two private estates. It may later be possible to find a British substitute for this.

GENTIAN is found on hilly pastures.

VERVAIN grows by roadsides and in hedge-banks.

IMPATIENS is not a native of this country, but grows to perfection along the banks of some of the Welsh rivers. The colour of the blossoms of this plant varies and only the beautiful pale mauve ones should be chosen.

WATER VIOLET is comparatively rare, but it is to be found in some of our slow-moving crystal brooks and streams.

THE FOUR HELPERS

It will be found that certain cases do not seem to fit exactly any one of the Twelve Healers, and many of these are such as those who have become so used to disease that it appears to be part of their nature; and it is difficult to see their true selves because, instead of seeking a cure, they have adapted themselves and altered their lives to suit the disease. Instead of being determined to conquer their illness, they have surrendered and looked upon their infirmity as inevitable, and have arranged their lives to fit in with their affliction.

Such people have lost much of their individuality, of their personality, and need to be helped out of the rut, out of the groove, in which they have become fixed before it is possible to know which of the Twelve Healers they need.

These cases, however, are not in reality hopeless, and for them there are Four Helpers, and these Four Helpers will lift them out of the state of stagnation into the state of activity. When they have progressed so far, their individuality will have sufficiently returned so that it will be possible to know which of the Twelve Healers will be required to bring them back to perfect health.

They are the people who say: "I have had this from a child, and cannot expect to lose it"; or who have been ill so long that they are resigned to the idea that nothing can be done; or it may be the people in whom, perhaps, bad temper or constant colds or the persistence of any ailment has come to be regarded as part of their nature. In fact, especially with certain states such as irritability, nervousness or shyness and such like conditions, it is accepted as part of their character, and they are really unconscious that it is not their real selves. And yet, for all such there is hope of better things if they desire it.

Resignation to faults in our character, or resignation to faults in our bodily health can be overcome if the wish is there to do so, and the Four Helpers get us over this stage and bring us into the range of the Twelve Healers. Of course, in all healing there must be a desire in the patient to get well.

These are four types of people who have lost hope, although they are not all conscious that they have done so; not conscious because, as has just been said, the abnormal state of mind or body is regarded both by themselves and others as part of their character. This, perhaps, applies more to the mental outlook towards life than in cases of physical defects, as we shall shortly see under the remedies of Heather and Rock Water.

ULEX EUROPÆUS

GORSE

They say: "I have tried everything and it is no use going on; nothing can cure me."

They have ceased to try, they are resigned to their infirmity, they do not even complain.

They say they have been told that nothing can be done, that they are past all medical help, and even if they do start treatment they say that they have been ill for so many months or years as the case may be, that they will not expect improvement for a long time.

The reason for their resignation is that at one time either fear or terror, or torture, made them give up hope and so they have ceased to strive. But yet such cases can improve beyond all expectations under the influence of Gorse; and then it may be found that Agrimony or Mimulus will be required to complete their cure.

Gorse is for those who have suffered much and whose courage, as it were, has failed; who have lost the heart to try any more.

People who need Gorse are generally sallow and rather darkish in complexion, often with dark lines beneath the eyes. They look as though they needed more sunshine in their lives to drive away the clouds.

QUERCUS PEDUNCULATA

OAK

Oak is for the type of people who, although they feel hopeless of any cure, still struggle and are irritated that they are ill.

These people have physical diseases which tend to go on for years and, although they feel quite hopeless about themselves, they still go on trying and struggling.

They are irritated that they cannot get well, and annoyed that they are ill because they are a trouble to others and not able to do their share in their daily duty.

They hate not being able to play their part in the game of life, and they think of themselves as failures.

These patients never blame others, they put all the responsibility upon themselves.

The illnesses of this type are where much balance is lost, mental and physical. Mental, such as severe nervous breakdowns, or such types of insanity which can be described as completely unbalanced (where there is great loss of control); and the same in the bodily state, where the patient loses control over parts of the body or its functions.

CALLUNA VULGARIS

HEATHER

The characteristic of the Heather people is that they worry over the troubles of others, not the big things of life, but the affairs of everyday.

They like to take care of those in trouble, and they are rather forcible in trying to do this. They become upset and excitable if they see others refusing their advice when they think it is for their good.

They try all means in their power to persuade or even compel others to do what they think right.

They mean very well indeed and their judgement is usually sound, but they strain themselves in wishing to hurry those of whom they are fond.

It is a state of over-anxiety for the welfare of friends and relations, and a forcible attempt to correct them.

This state of mind is so much part of their natures that it comes to be regarded as their character.

The Heather people tend to suffer from heart-trouble, palpitations, throbbing headaches, indigestion and such complaints as may be caused by anxious excitement and intense effort to help in the ordinary affairs of life.

Their diseases are often not very severe until towards old age, but they may suffer a considerable amount of inconvenience and interference with their daily life for years at a time through minor maladies. They are inclined also to be a little afraid for themselves if they get even slight trouble.

They like people to be dependent upon them, and they take pleasure in feeling that they are being of use and help to any in difficulty.

They are so self-confident and certainly very capable, that they never doubt their ability to advise and to render assistance.

Heather people are often well-built and of high colour, full-blooded, strong in body and full of energy and activity, and are unsparing of themselves in exertions for others.

This remedy can much improve their health, calm their fears and soothe their anxieties over the concern of those in whom they are interested.

ROCK WATER

These people are people of ideals. They have very strong opinions about religion or politics, or reform.

Well-meaning enough and wishing to see the world different and better, they tend to confine their efforts of help to criticism instead of example.

They allow their minds and largely their lives to be ruled by their theories.

Any failure to make others follow their ideas brings them much unhappiness.

They want to plan the world according to their own outlook, instead of quietly and gently doing a little in the Great Plan.

This remedy brings great peace and understanding, broadens the outlook that all people must find perfection in their own individual way, and brings the realisation of 'being' and not 'doing'; of being in ourselves a reflection of Great Things and not attempting to put forward our own ideas.

It teaches that it is by gentle example people are helped and are brought to realise truth, not by the severe methods of the inquisitor.

It helps to abolish disapproval and brings the understanding of allowing everyone to gain their own experiences and find their own salvation.

The blooms of the Gorse should be taken just before the plant reaches its full glory, a little before it gives out scent; depending, of course, upon the season, but probably about the middle of April.

The small slender flower-stems of the Oak should be gathered in full bloom, again depending on the weather, but somewhere early or middle May.

The Heather to choose is not the red bell-heather, but the beautiful slender small rose-pink variety such as grows on the Welsh or Scottish mountains in August and September. Heather should be prepared after midday, whereas all the other remedies mentioned in this book should be started in the morning.

Rock Water. It has long been known that certain well- and spring-waters have had the power to heal a limited number of people, and such wells or springs have become renowned for this property. Any well or any spring which has been known to be a healing centre and which is still left free in its natural state, unhampered by the shrines of man, may be used. This remedy does not require long exposure to sunshine, about half-an-hour being sufficient.

For those unable to prepare their own stocks, the chemists mentioned below have very kindly undertaken the distribution of these remedies at a most moderate price.

> KEENE & ASHWELL LTD,
> 57B New Cavendish Street,
> London, W1.

> NELSON & CO., LTD,
> 73 Duke Street,
> Grosvenor Square,
> London, W1.

The Set of Twelve Stock Remedies, 5s. Single remedies, 8d. Postage 4d.

The Set of Four Helpers, 2s. 6d. Postage 3d.

And may we ever have joy and gratitude in our hearts that the Great Creator of all things, in His Love for us, has placed the herbs in the fields for our healing.

— VII —

The Story of the Travellers

[1934]

Once upon a time; and it is always once upon a time, sixteen travellers set out to journey through a forest.

At first all went well, but after they had journeyed some distance one of the number, Agrimony, began to be worried as to whether they were on the right path. Later in the afternoon as they went deeper into the shadows, Mimulus began to be afraid, afraid that they had lost the road. When the sun set and the shadows deepened and the night-noises of the forest were heard around them, Rock Rose became full of terror and was in a state of panic. In the middle of the night when all was blackness, Gorse lost all hope and said, "I can go no further; you go along, but I shall stay here as I am until death relieves my sufferings."

Oak, on the other hand, though feeling all was lost and that they would never again see the sunshine said, "I shall struggle on to the very last," and he did in a wild way.

Scleranthus had some hope but at times he suffered so from uncertainty and indecision, first wanting to take one road and almost at once another. Clematis plodded on quietly and patiently, but caring oh so little if he fell into the last sound sleep or whether he got out of the forest. Gentian at times much cheered the party, but at others fell into a state of despondency and depression.

Others of the travellers never feared but that they would get through and in their own way wanted so much to help their companions.

Heather was very sure he knew the path and wanted all the company to take his way. Chicory had no concern about the end of the journey but was full of solicitude as to whether his fellows were footsore or tired or had enough to eat. Cerato had not much confidence in his judgement and wanted to try every path to be sure they were not wrong, and meek little Centaury so wanted to lighten the burden that he was ready to carry everybody's baggage. Unfortunately for little Centaury, he generally carried the burden of those most able to bear their own because they called the loudest.

Rock Water, all afire to help, a little depressed the party because he would criticise what they were doing wrong, and yet Rock Water knew the way. Vervain should also have known the path well enough, but although he had become a little confused, held forth at length as to the only way out of the wood. Impatiens, too, well knew the pathway home, so well that he was impatient with those less speedy than himself. Water Violet had travelled that way before and knew the right road and yet was a little proud and a little disdainful that others did not understand. Water Violet thought them a little inferior.

And in the end they all came through the forest.

Now they go as guides to other travellers who have not made the journey before, and, because they know there is a pathway through, and because they know the darkness of the forest is but the shadows of the night, they walk as "gentlemen unafraid," and each of the sixteen sojourners teach in their own way the lesson, the example needed.

Agrimony strides along free of all care, and jests on everything. Mimulus can know no fear; Rock Rose in the darkest moments is just a picture of calm, serene courage. Gorse in the blackest night tells them of the progress they will make when the sun rises in the morning.

Oak stands steadfast in the strongest gale; Scleranthus walks with perfect certainty; the eyes of Clematis are fixed with joy on the journey's end, and no difficulties or set-backs can discourage Gentian.

Heather has learnt that each traveller must walk in his own way and quietly strides in front to show it can be done. Chicory, always waiting to lend a hand, but only when asked, and then so quietly. Cerato knows so well the little paths that lead to nowhere, and Centaury ever seeks the weakest who find their burden heavy.

Rock Water has forgotten to accuse, he just spends all the time encouraging. Vervain no longer preaches but silently points the way. Impatiens knows no hurry but lingers amongst the hindmost to keep their pace; and Water Violet, more like an angel than a man, passes amongst the company like a breath of warm wind or a ray of glorious sunshine, blessing everyone.

— VIII —

Twelve Healers

[Printed* at Epsom, 1933]

To many of us who have used the following remedies their power to
heal is well-known; and the results obtained have passed our expectations. Hundreds of so-called incurable cases have been brought back
to health and happiness.

These remedies are prescribed according to the mental condition of
the patient, utterly and entirely ignoring the physical disease.

The twelve indications are as follows:

1.	TORMENTED	Agrimony
2.	TERROR	Rock Rose
3.	FEAR	Mimulus
4.	INDIFFERENCE	Clematis
5.	PAIN	Impatiens
6.	INDECISION	Scleranthus
7.	THE ENTHUSIAST	Vervain
8.	DISCOURAGEMENT	Gentian
9.	THE DOORMAT	Centaury
10.	THE FOOL	Cerato
11.	GRIEF	Water Violet
12.	CONGESTION	Chicory

Fundamentally there are twelve primary types of personality, and
there is a positive and a negative of each.

These types of personality are indicated to us by the moon according to which sign of the Zodiac she is in at birth, and a study of this
will give us the following points:

* This article probably appeared in *The Naturopathic Journal*.

1. The type of personality.
2. His object and his work in life.
3. The remedy which will assist him in that work.

We, as healers, are dealing only with the negatives of the twelve types.

The secret of life is to be true to our personality, not to suffer interference from outside influences.

Our personality we learn from the position of the moon at birth; our dangers of interference from the planets. But astrologers too much emphasise the planets, for, if we can hold our personality, be true unto ourselves, we need fear no planetary or outside influence. The remedies assist us to maintain our personality.

It is only in the earlier stages of our evolution that we are directly assisted and ruled by one or more planets. Once we develop love, that is the great love of our fellowmen, we free ourselves from our stars, we lose our line of fate, and for better or for worse we steer our own ship.

What Hahnemann, Culpepper and the other great seekers have been striving to find is the worldly mental reaction which indicates these twelve personalities, and the remedies which belong to each.

We have twelve remedies; how simple it now is to prescribe with accuracy, and to explain to our patients the reason of their disharmony, their discord, their disease, and to point out to them the simple message, the lesson, to bring themselves again in tune with the Infinity of their souls, and restore them to mental and physical health.

There are seven steps in healing in the following order:

PEACE
HOPE
JOY
FAITH
CERTAINTY
WISDOM
LOVE

And once love enters into the patient, not self-love, but the love of the Universe, then he has turned his back on what we have called disease.

The CLEMATIS people are *indifferent,* and have not sufficient interest in life. They are apathetic and make no real endeavour to recover from illness or to concentrate on their daily work. They often like much sleep, and have a far-away look in their eyes.

The AGRIMONY folk are inwardly *tormented* by worries and anxieties, though outwardly they make a brave show to hide the strain. Frequently they drink heavily or give way to drugs to help them stand the stress.

The SCLERANTHUS people are full of *indecision*. They find it difficult to make up their minds in ordinary life, and in illness they are uncertain as to what they want, first thinking one thing right and then another.

CERATO are the *foolish*. They should be wise teachers and instructors, but they seem to listen too much to other opinions, and be too easily influenced by outside circumstances.

IMPATIENS is *pain* of severe type caused by the blocking of a channel which should be admitting spiritual light and truth. It is often some cruelty in the nature which causes this.

CENTAURY are the *doormats*. They seem to lack all power of individuality or the ability to resist being used by everyone. They put up no struggle whatever to gain their freedom.

WATERVIOLET is *grief* of such a type as belongs only to big souls who, with courage and resignation, bravely and uncomplainingly bear their sorrow without any annoyance to others, or allowing it to interfere with their life's work.

MIMULUS is full of *fear*. These people try feebly to escape their persecutors, but they seem hypnotised, and silently and without resistance suffer their fear. They generally make excuses for themselves.

VERVAIN is the *enthusiast*. Those people who strive too hard to attain their ideals, and in so doing hurt themselves. They are those who are aiming high, but instead of using gentleness and patience use energy and hurry. They are the people who have advanced sufficiently to realise that big ideals are only attained without stress or hurry.

CHICORY are the folk who desire to serve, who have the love aspect well developed, and yet allow outside influences to check the outflow of their love, and so become mentally and perhaps also physically *congested*.

GENTIAN is *discouragement*. People again who wish to do much, and yet allow themselves to get under the influence of doubt or depression when difficulties arise. Often they desire things to go too much their own way, instead of seeing the bigger outlook.

ROCK ROSE is *terror;* terror of something greater than material things; terror of death, suicide, or of super-natural forces. They are the people who are putting up a fight for mental freedom.

If we now think of the twelve attributes of Christ which we most wish to attain, and which He came to teach us, we find the twelve great lessons of life.

And, whilst we are, of course, learning them all, no doubt we are concentrating on one in particular. This is indicated by the moon at our birth, showing us the main object of our life.

Remedy	*Quality to develop*	*Fault*
Agrimony	Stillness	Tormented
Scleranthus	Steadfastness	Indecision
Vervain	Tolerance	The Enthusiast
Clematis	Gentleness	Indifference
Chicory	Love	Congestion
Gentian	Understanding	Discouragement
Water Violet	Joy	Grief
Centaury	Power	The Doormat
Impatiens	Forgiveness	Pain
Cerato	Wisdom	The Fool
Rock Rose	Courage	Terror
Mimulus	Sympathy	Fear

Stocks of these remedies can be obtained from the leading homœopathic chemists, though they can be prepared as follows by anyone who cares to make their own.

Take a thin glass bowl, fill with clear water from a stream or spring for preference, and float enough of the blooms of the plant to cover the surface. Allow this to stand in bright sunshine until the flowers begin to wilt. Very gently pick out the blooms, pour the water into bottles and add an equal quantity of brandy as a preservative.

One drop alone of this is sufficient to make potent an eight ounce bottle of water, from which doses may be taken by the tea-spoonful as required.

The doses should be taken as the patient feels necessary: hourly in acute cases; three or four times a day in chronic cases until relief occurs when they can be dispensed with.

Clematis, the Traveller's Joy, adorns our hedges where there is chalk. Agrimony and Vervain we find by the sides of our lanes: Chicory and Scleranthus amongst the cornfields. Centaury, Gentian and Rock Rose in meadow-land. Mimulus Luteus and Impatiens Royalei both grow to perfection near Crichowell, a few miles from Abergavenny, though the former can be found in other counties. Ceratostigma is not found wild in this country, but there are plants in the gardens of the 'Pleasaunce,' Overstrand, Norfolk, and in Kew Gardens. Water Violet can be found in our very clear beautiful streams.

May we ever praise God that in His mercy he placed herbs in the field for our healing.

— IX —

Twelve Great Remedies

[*Heal Thyself*, February, 1933]

The twelve remedies which I have been working on for the last five years are proving so wonderful in their curative results and they are bringing health to so many so-called incurables, even where homœopathic treatment has failed, that I am endeavouring to make the prescribing so simple that they can be used by all lay people. The remedies themselves never give strong reactions, since they never do harm, however much is taken and if they wrong remedy is given, no bad effect will follow, but when the right one is given benefit will be obtained. None of the plants from which these remedies are extracted are poisonous. They are all beneficent. Therefore no one need be in fear of using them.

The whole principle is this: that there are twelve mental states, and to each of these states belongs a herb. No matter whether the disease is of the utmost severity or a slight cold, whether it is of an hour's or of many years' duration, it matters not; it is the mental state, and that alone, which decides the choice of the remedy required.

The mental states and the corresponding remedies are as follows:

1. In cases of great urgency, great danger, intense fear or terror or depression, in all cases of utmost need *when the situation seem desperate* give ROCK ROSE.

2. When there is fear, not terror, but *quite calm fear* give MIMULUS.

3. When the patient is *restless, anxious,* tortured give AGRIMONY.

4. When there is indecision, *when nothing seems right,* when first one thing and then another is required give SCLERANTHUS.

5. When the patient is *sleepy, drowsy, listless,* a far-away look, with no interest in things, making no effort to get well, no joy in life give CLEMATIS.

6. When there is *self-pity,* patient feels badly treated, that the suffering is undeserved give CHICORY.

7. The patient who *wants to do foolish things,* listens to everyone's advice, who tries any and every cure suggested requires CERATO.

8. The patient who is *discouraged,* who is doing well but looks on the dark side of things and feels *depressed* requires GENTIAN.

9. The *strong-willed,* those who are *difficult to treat* because they *always know best* and go their own way require VERVAIN.

10. When there is *impatience, severe pain,* fretting to be quickly well, anxious to be up and about again, impatient with those around give IMPATIENS.

11. Those calm, quiet and *brave patients who never complain,* who in their sickness desire to be of no trouble to others and strive to get well by themselves will be helped by WATER VIOLET.

12. Those who are *weak, pale and have no strength,* just feeble and tired will be much helped by CENTAURY.

The dosage is as follows: take two or three drops of the stock remedy to an ordinary medicine bottle, fill it with water, shake up well, then give teaspoonfuls of this as required. In urgent cases every quarter of an hour, in serious cases every hour, and in ordinary cases three or four times a day. In cases of unconsciousness, the lips of the patient may be moistened with the remedy.

As the patient improves, it will often be found necessary to change the remedy as his state changes, and in some cases even as many as half a dozen different herbs may be required.

As an example.

A man of thirty-five had had severe rheumatism for five weeks. When first seen almost every joint in the body was affected with swelling and tenderness, he was in great pain, rolling about in his torture, anxious as to what was going to happen. The patient was very ill and looked as though he would not be able to stand much more.

Agrimony was given hourly for twenty hours when there was marked improvement, pain and swelling had all gone except for one shoulder joint, the patient was calmer and less worried. *Agrimony* was continued for another six hours when the patient slept for four hours. On waking all pain had gone. The next stage was one of fear, fear of the pain coming back, fear of moving in case it caused a recurrence. *Mimulus* was given, and the next day the patient was up and dressed and had shaved himself. In spite of the good result, the patient felt discouraged, down-hearted. *Gentian* was given and on the third day the patient was out and about, he attended a cinema and also visited the local tavern.

At other times a single remedy is all that is required as in the following case. A girl of eighteen had had some large cysts removed from her thyroid gland in the neck six months previously. These were returning and she was told that she must wait until they were big again when another operation would be necessary. She was a gentle little girl of the day-dreaming type, living in a land of dreams and very little concerned about her condition. *Clematis*, given three times a day for a week, caused complete absorption of the cysts, and up to a date, three months afterwards, there has been no sign of recurrence, and no further doses have been necessary.

A lady had had acute rheumatism for two years, and had been either in nursing homes or hospitals the whole of that time. When first seen, the hands were very stiff and painful, the ankles were double their normal size and the patient was only just able to walk. In addition, there was pain in the shoulders, neck and back. The lady was one of exquisite gentleness, calmness and courage, and had borne her illness with wonderful patience and fortitude. *Water Violet* was clearly indicated and it was given for two weeks, definite improvement slowly occurring. Then came a period of slight self-pity which *Chicory* removed. At the end of four weeks the patient was able to walk two miles, but felt unsteady and uncertain, so *Schleranthus* was given. Then followed a period of a little impatience and wanting to be back doing everything which indicated *Impatiens*. At the end of eight weeks the patient could walk four miles, could use her hands freely, had no pain and, with the exception of a little stiffness and a trace of swelling in the right ankle, was completely cured.

A lady of about forty had had vague pains in the abdomen for three weeks, and she had rapid swelling of the glands in the groin, armpits and neck. On examination there were found large masses of swollen glands in the abdomen and the blood count was that of an acute lymphatic leukæmia. The outlook was of course extremely serious. The patient realized that she had a malignant disease. She was in terror and was secretly thinking of the easiest way to commit suicide. *Rock Rose* was given for a few days with lessening of the abdominal pain and a diminution in the size of the glands. The patient's attitude then changed, she was encouraged by the improvement and the black dread and terror of death had gone, but there was now a quiet fear that it was too good to be true, hence *Mimulus* was given for about two weeks, at the end of which time the patient's condition was normal and she has remained perfectly fit ever since, a period of six months.

A farmer suffered from paralysis of the neck so that the head fell forward. Besides there was weakening of the eye and mouth muscles. He was intensely strong-willed, would go about his work as usual, for months refused treatment. *Vervain* effected a complete cure in about two weeks.

A lady of about forty had suffered from asthma from childhood, and had spent about four months each winter in bed. She had had an enormous number of injections of adrenalin and had been given every type of asthma treatment without effect. She was, like many cases of asthma, whooping cough, and other chest complaints, tortured by her disease. She was first seen in December, 1930, and by the end of January 1931, *Agrimony* had completely removed the disease. There was a slight return in the winter of 1931 which was easily controlled, the patient not having to go to bed. Since then there has been no trace whatever of the disease.

*

[*Heal Thyself*, May, 1933]

MY TWELVE REMEDIES

By Dr Edward Bach

In reply to the questions which were asked in *Heal Thyself* by Dr Emil Schleger and Dr Petrie Hoyle I would state the following:

The Latin names of the twelve remedies are as follows:

1. ROCK ROSE......................	*Helianthemum vulgare*
2. MIMULUS........................	*Mimulus luteus*
3. AGRIMONY	*Agrimonia eupatoria*
4. SCLERANTHUS	*Scleranthus annuus*
5. CLEMATIS	*Clematis vitalba*
6. CHICORY........................	*Cichorium intybus*
7. CERATO	*Ceratostigma Willmottiana*
8. GENTIAN	*Gentiana amarella*
9. VERVAIN	*Verbena officinalis*
10. IMPATIENS	*Impatiens royalei*
11. WATER VIOLET	*Hottonia palustris*
12. CENTAURY	*Erythraea centaurium*

These plants are in flower mostly during the months of July, August and September. Water Violet is a little earlier, being at its prime in June and July.

The following are situations where they may be found:

ROCK ROSE	Upland pastures.
MIMULUS	Is comparatively rare, but grows on the edges of streams and marshes where the water is clear.
AGRIMONY	Grows throughout the country in hedgebanks and meadows.
SCLERANTHUS	Can be found amongst and around the edges of some cornfields.
CLEMATIS	Adorns our hedges in many parts of the country where there is chalk.
CHICORY	Cornfields and cultivated ground, in some parts it is grown by farmers.
CERATO	Is not a native of this country and is only to be found on one or two private estates. It may later be possible to find a British substitute for this.
GENTIAN	Is found on hilly pastures.
VERVAIN	Grows by roadsides and in hedgebanks.
IMPATIENS	Is not a native of this country, but grows to perfection along the banks of some of the Welsh rivers. The colour of the blossoms of this plant varies, and only the beautiful pale mauve ones should be chosen.

WATER VIOLET   Is comparatively rare, but is to be found in some
                of our slow moving crystal brooks and streams.
CENTAURY   Grows in the meadows, hedgebanks and pasture
                land.

Method of preparation. The remedies should be prepared near the
place where the plant grows, as the flowers should be put straight into
the water after gathering, whilst they are quite fresh and full of life.

A thin glass bowl is taken, filled with clear water, preferably from a
pure spring or stream. Sufficient blooms of the plant are floated on the
water to cover the surface, as much as can be done without over-
lapping the blossoms. Then allow to stand in bright sunshine until the
blooms show signs of fading. The time varies from about two to seven
hours, according to the plant, and the strength of the sun. The
blossoms are then gently lifted out, and the water poured into bottles,
with an equal quantity of brandy, added as a preservative. Two or
three drops of this are sufficient to activate an ordinary medicine
bottle of water, from which doses of a teaspoonful may be taken as
required.

– X –

Free Thyself

[1932]

INTRODUCTION

It is impossible to put truth into words. The author of this book has no desire to preach, indeed he very greatly dislikes that method of conveying knowledge. He has tried, in the following pages, to show as clearly and simply as possible the purpose of our lives, the uses of the difficulties that beset us, and the means by which we can regain our health; and, in fact, how each of us may become our own doctor.

CHAPTER ONE

It is as simple as this, the Story of Life.

A small child has decided to paint the picture of a house in time for her mother's birthday. In her little mind the house is already painted; she knows what it is to be like down to the very smallest detail, there remains only to put it on paper.

Out comes the paint-box, the brush and the paint-rag, and full of enthusiasm and happiness she sets to work. Her whole attention and interest is centred on what she is doing – nothing can distract her from the work in hand.

The picture is finished in time for the birthday. To the very best of her ability she has put her idea of a house into form. It is a work of art because it is all her very own, every stroke done out of love for her mother, every window, every door painted in with the conviction that it is meant to be there. Even if it looks like a haystack, it is the most perfect house that has ever been painted: it is a success because the little artist has put her whole heart and soul, her whole being into the doing of it.

This is health, this is success and happiness and true service. Serving through love in perfect freedom in our own way.

So we come down into this world, knowing what picture we have to paint, having already mapped out of our path through life, and all that remains for us to do is to put it into material form. We pass along full of joy and interest, concentrating all our attention upon the perfecting of that picture, and to the very best of our ability translating our own thoughts and aims into the physical life of whatever environment we have chosen.

Then, if we follow from start to finish our very own ideals, our very own desires with all the strength we possess, there is no failure, our life has been a tremendous success, a healthy and a happy one.

The same little story of the child-painter will illustrate how, if we allow them, the difficulties of life may interfere with this success and happiness and health, and deter us from our purpose.

The child is busily and happily painting when someone comes along and says, "Why not put a window here, and a door there; and of course the garden path should go this way." The result in the child will be complete loss of interest in the work; she may go on, but is now only putting someone else's ideas on paper: she may become cross, irritated, unhappy, afraid to refuse these suggestions; begin to hate the picture and perhaps tear it up: in fact, according to the type of child so will be the reaction.

The final picture may be a recognisable house, but it is an imperfect one and a failure because it is the interpretation of another's thoughts, not the child's. It is of no use as a birthday present because it may not be done in time, and the mother may have to wait another whole year for her gift.

This is disease, the reaction to interference. This is temporary failure and unhappiness: and this occurs when we allow others to interfere with our purpose in life, and implant in our minds doubt, or fear, or indifference.

CHAPTER TWO

Health depends on being in harmony with our souls.

It is of primary importance that the true meaning of health and of disease should be clearly understood.

Health is our heritage, our right. It is the complete and full union between soul, mind and body; and this is no difficult far-away ideal to attain, but one so easy and natural that many of us have overlooked it. All earthly things are but the interpretation of things spiritual. The smallest most insignificant occurrence has a Divine purpose behind it.

We each have a Divine mission in this world, and our souls use our minds and bodies as instruments to do this work, so that when all three are working in unison the result is perfect health and perfect happiness.

A Divine mission means no sacrifice, no retiring from the world, no rejecting of the joys of beauty and nature; on the contrary, it means a fuller and greater enjoyment of all things: it means doing the work that we love to do with all our heart and soul, whether it be house-keeping, farming, painting, acting, or serving our fellow-men in shops or houses. And this work, whatever it may be, if we love it above all else, is the definite command of our soul, the work we have to do in this world, and in which alone we can be our true selves, interpreting in an ordinary materialistic way the message of that true self.

We can judge, therefore, by our health and by our happiness, how well we are interpreting this message.

There are all the spiritual attributes in the perfect man; and we come into this world to manifest these one at a time, to perfect and strengthen them so that no experience, no difficulty can weaken or deflect us from the fulfilment of this purpose. We chose the earthly occupation, and the external circumstances that will give us the best opportunities of testing us to the full: we come with the full realisation of our particular work: we come with the unthinkable privilege of knowing that all our battles are won before they are fought, that victory is certain before ever the test arrives, because we know that we are the children of the Creator, and as such are Divine, unconquerable and invincible. With this knowledge life is a joy; hardships and experiences can be looked upon as adventures, for we have but to realise our power, to be true to our Divinity, when these melt away like mist in the sunshine. God did indeed give His children dominion over all things.

Our souls will guide us, if we will only listen, in every circumstance, every difficulty; and the mind and body so directed will pass through life radiating happiness and perfect health, as free from all cares and responsibilities as the small trusting child.

CHAPTER THREE

Our souls are perfect, being children of the Creator, and everything they tell us to do is for our good.

Health is, therefore, the true realisation of what we are: we are perfect: we are children of God. There is no striving to gain what we have already attained. We are merely here to manifest in material form the perfection with which we have been endowed from the beginning of all time. Health is listening solely to the commands of our souls; in being trustful as little children; in rejecting intellect (that tree of the knowledge of good and evil) with its reasonings, its 'fors' and 'againsts,' its anticipatory fears: ignoring convention, the trivial ideas and commands of other people, so that we can pass through life untouched, unharmed, free to serve our fellow-men.

We can judge our health by our happiness, and by our happiness we can know that we are obeying the dictates of our souls. It is not necessary to be a monk, a nun, or hide away from the world; the world is for us to enjoy and to serve, and it is only by serving out of love and happiness that we can truly be of use, and do our best work. A thing done from a sense of duty with, perhaps, a feeling of irritation and impatience is of no account at all, it is merely precious time wasted when there might be a brother in real need of our help.

Truth has no need to be analysed, argued about, or wrapped up in many words. It is realised in a flash, it is part of you. It is only about the unessential complicated things of life that we need so much convincing, and that have led to the development of the intellect. The things that count are simple, they are the ones that make you say, "why, that is true, I seem to have known that always," and so is the realisation of the happiness that comes to us when we are in harmony with our spiritual self, and the closer the union the more intense the joy. Think of the radiance one sometimes sees in a bride on her wedding morn; the rapture of a mother with a new-born babe; the ecstasy of an artist completing a masterpiece: such are the moments where there is spiritual union.

Think how wonderful life would be if we lived it all in such joy: and so it is possible when we lose ourselves in our life's work.

CHAPTER FOUR

If we follow our own instincts, our own wishes, our own thoughts, our own desires, we should never know anything but joy and health.

Neither is it a difficult far-away attainment to hear the voice of our own soul; it has all been made so simple for us if we will but acknowledge it. Simplicity is the keynote of all Creation.

Our soul (the still small voice, God's own voice) speaks to us through our intuition, our instincts, through our desires, ideals, our ordinary likes and dislikes; in whichever way it is easiest for us individually to hear. How else can He speak to us? Our true instincts, desires, likes or dislikes are given us so that we can interpret the spiritual commands of our soul by means of our limited physical perceptions, for it is not possible for many of us yet to be in direct communion with our Higher Self. These commands are meant to be followed implicitly, because the soul alone knows what experiences are necessary for that particular personality. Whatever the command may be, trivial or important, the desire for another cup of tea, or a complete change of the whole of one's life's habits, it should be willingly obeyed. The soul knows that satisfaction is the one real-cure for all that we, in this world, consider as sin and wrong, for until the whole being revolts against a certain act, that fault is not eradicated but simply dormant, just as it is much better and quicker to go on sticking one's fingers into the jam-pot until one is so sick that jam has no further attraction.

Our true desires, the wishes of our true selves, are not to be confused with the wishes and desires of other people so often implanted in our minds, or of conscience, which is another word for the same thing. We must pay no heed to the world's interpretation of our actions. Our own soul alone is responsible for our good, our reputation is in His keeping; we can rest assured that there is only one sin, that of not obeying the dictates of our own Divinity. That is the sin against God and our neighbour. These wishes, intuitions, desires are never selfish; they concern ourselves alone and are always right for us, and bring us health in body and mind.

Disease is the result in the physical body of the resistance of the personality to the guidance of the soul. It is when we turn a deaf ear to the 'still small voice', and forget the Divinity within us; when we try to force our wishes upon others, or allow their suggestions, thoughts, and commands to influence us.

The more we become free from outside influences, from other personalities, the more our soul can use us to do His work.

It is only when we attempt to control and rule someone else that we are selfish. But the world tries to tell us that it is selfishness to follow our own desires. That is because the world wishes to enslave us, for truly it is only when we can realise and be unhampered our real selves that we can be used for the good of mankind. It is the great truth of Shakespeare, "To thine own self be true, and it must follow, as the night the day, thou canst not then be false to any man."

The bee, by its very choice of a particular flower for its honey, is the means used to bring it the pollen necessary for the future life of its young plants.

CHAPTER FIVE

It is allowing the interference of other people that stops our listening to the dictates of our soul, and that brings disharmony and disease. The moment the thought of another person enters our minds, it deflects us from our true course.

God gave us each our birthright, an individuality of our very own: He gave us each our own particular work to do, which only we can do: He gave us each our own particular path to follow with which nothing must interfere. Let us see to it that not only do we allow no interference, but, and even more important, that we in no way whatsoever interfere with any other single human being. In this lies true health, true service, and the fulfilment of our purpose on earth.

Interferences occur in every life, they are part of the Divine Plan, they are necessary so that we can learn to stand up to them: in fact, we can look upon them as really useful opponents, merely there to help us gain in strength, and realise our Divinity and our invincibility. And we can also know that it is only when we allow them to affect us that they gain in importance and tend to check our progress. It rests entirely with us how quickly we progress: whether we allow interference in our Divine mission; whether we accept the manifestation of interference (called disease) and let it limit and injure our bodies; or whether, we, as children of God, use these to establish us the more firmly in our purpose.

The more the apparent difficulties in our path the more we may be certain that our mission is worth while. Florence Nightingale reached her ideal in the face of a nation's opposition: Galileo believed the world was round in spite of the entire world's disbelief, and the ugly duckling became the swan although his whole family scorned him.

We have no right whatever to interfere with the life of any one of God's children. Each of us has our own job, in the doing of which only we have the power and knowledge to bring it to perfection. It is only when we forget this fact, and try and force our work on others, or let them interfere with ours that friction and disharmony occur in our being.

This disharmony, disease, makes itself manifest in the body for the body merely serves to reflect the workings of the soul; just as the face reflects happiness by smiles, or temper by frowns. And so in bigger things; the body will reflect the true causes of disease (which are such as fear, indecision, doubt, etc.) in the disarrangement of its systems and tissues.

Disease, therefore, is the result of interference: interfering with someone else or allowing ourselves to be interfered with.

CHAPTER SIX

All we have to do is to preserve our personality, to live our own life, to be captain of our own ship, and all will be well.

There are great qualities in which all men are gradually perfecting themselves, possibly concentrating upon one or two at a time. They are those which have been manifested in the earthly lives of all the Great Masters who have, from time to time, come into the world to teach us, and help us to see the easy and simple way of overcoming all our difficulties.

These are such as:

LOVE
SYMPATHY
PEACE
STEADFASTNESS
GENTLENESS
STRENGTH
UNDERSTANDING
TOLERANCE
WISDOM
FORGIVENESS
COURAGE
JOY

And it is by perfecting these qualities in ourselves that each one of us is raising the whole world a step near to its final unthinkably glorious goal. We realise then that we are seeking no selfish gain of personal merit, but that every single human being, rich or poor, high or low, is of the same importance in the Divine Plan, and is given the same mighty privilege of being a saviour of the world simply by knowing that he is a perfect child of the Creator.

As there are these qualities, these steps to perfection, so there are hindrances, or interferences which serve to strengthen us in our determination to stand firm.

These are the real causes of disease, and are of such as:

RESTRAINT
FEAR
RESTLESSNESS
INDECISION
INDIFFERENCE
WEAKNESS
DOUBT
OVER-ENTHUSIASM
IGNORANCE
IMPATIENCE
TERROR
GRIEF

These, if we allow them, will reflect themselves in the body causing what we call disease. Not understanding the real causes we have attributed disharmony to external influences, germs, cold, heat, and have given names to the results, arthritis, cancer, asthma, etc.: thinking that disease begins in the physical body.

There are then definite groups of mankind, each group performing its own function, that is, manifesting in the material world the particular lesson he has learnt. Each individual in these groups has a definite personality of his own, a definite work to do, and a definite individual way of doing that work. These are also causes of disharmony, which unless we hold to our definite personality and our work, may react upon the body in the form of disease.

Real health is happiness, and a happiness so easy of attainment because it is a happiness in small things; doing the things that we really do love to do, being with the people that we truly like. There is no strain, no effort, no striving for the unattainable, health is there for us to accept any time we like. It is to find out and do the work that we are really suited for. So many suppress their real desires and become square pegs in round holes: through the wishes of a parent a son may become a solicitor, a soldier, a business man, when his true desire is to become a carpenter: or through the ambitions of a mother to see her daughter well married, the world may lose another Florence Nightingale. This sense of duty is then a false sense of duty, and a dis-service to the world; it results in unhappiness and, probably, the greater part of a lifetime wasted before the mistake can be rectified.

There was a Master once Who said, "Know ye not that I must be about My Father's business?" meaning that He must obey His Divinity and not His earthly parents.

Let us find the one thing in life that attracts us most and do it. Let that one thing be so part of us that it is as natural as breathing; as natural as it is for the bee to collect honey, and the tree to shed its old leaves in the autumn and bring forth new ones in the spring. If we study nature we find that every creature, bird, tree and flower has its definite part to play, its own definite and peculiar work through which it aids and enriches the entire Universe. The very worm, going about its daily job, helps to drain and purify the earth: the earth provides for the nutriment of all green things; and, in turn, vegetation sustains mankind and every living creature, returning in due course to enrich the soil. Their life is one of beauty and usefulness, their work is so natural to them that it is their life.

And our own work, when we find it, so belongs to us, so fits us, that it is effortless, it is easy, it is a joy: we never tire of it, it is our hobby. It brings out in us our true personality, all the talents and capabilities waiting within each one of us to be manifested: in it we are happy and at home; and it is only when we are happy (which is obeying the commands of our soul) that we can do our best work.

We may have already found our right work, then what fun life is! Some from childhood have the knowledge of what they are meant to do, and keep to it throughout their lives: and some know in childhood, but are deterred by contra-suggestions and circumstances, and the discouragement of others. Yet we can all get back to our ideals, and even though we cannot realise them immediately we can go on seeking to do so, then the very seeking will bring us comfort, for our souls are very patient with us. The right desire, the right motive, no matter what the result, is the thing that counts, the real success.

So if you would rather be a farmer than a lawyer; if you would rather be a barber than a bus-driver, or a cook than a greengrocer, change your occupation, be what you want to be: and then you will be happy and well, then you will work with zest, and then you will be doing finer work as a farmer, a barber, a cook, than you could ever achieve in the occupation that never belonged to you.

And then you will be obeying the dictates of your Spiritual self.

CHAPTER SEVEN

Once we realise our own Divinity the rest is easy.

In the beginning God gave man dominion over all things. Man, the child of the Creator, has a deeper reason for his disharmony than the draught from an open window. "Our fault lies not in our stars, but in ourselves," and how full of gratitude and hope can we be when we realise that the cure also lies within ourselves! Remove the disharmony, the fear, the terror, or the indecision, and we regain harmony between soul and mind, and the body is once more perfect in all its parts.

Whatever the disease, the result of this disharmony, we may be quite sure that the cure is well within our powers of accomplishment, for our souls never ask of us more than we can very easily do.

Everyone of us is a healer, because everyone of us at heart has a love for something, for our fellow-men, for animals, for nature, for beauty in some form, and we every one of us wish to protect and help it to increase. Everyone of us also has sympathy with those in distress, and naturally so, because we have all been in distress ourselves at some time in our lives. So that not only can we heal ourselves, but we have the great privilege of being able to help others to heal themselves, and the only qualifications necessary are love and sympathy.

We, as children of the Creator, have within us all perfection, and we come into this world merely that we may realise our Divinity; so that all tests and all experiences will leave us untouched, for through that Divine Power all things are possible to us.

CHAPTER EIGHT

The healing herbs are those which have been given the power to help us preserve our personality.

Just as God in His mercy has given us food to eat, so has He placed amongst the herbs of the fields beautiful plants to heal us when we are sick. These are there to extend a helping hand to man in those dark hours of forgetfulness when he loses sight of his Divinity, and allows the cloud of fear or pain to obscure his vision.

Such herbs are:

CHICORY	*Chichorium intybus*
MIMULUS	*Mimulus luteus*
AGRIMONY	*Agrimonia eupatoria*
SCLERANTHUS	*Scleranthus annuus*
CLEMATIS	*Clematis vitalba*
CENTAURY	*Erythræa centaurium*
GENTIAN	*Gentiana amarella*
VERVAIN	*Verbena officinalis*
CERATO	*Ceratostigma willmottiana*
IMPATIENS	*Impatiens royalei*
ROCK ROSE	*Helianthemum vulgare*
WATER VIOLET	*Hottonia palustris*

Each herb corresponds with one of the qualities, and its purpose is to strengthen that quality so that the personality may rise above the fault that is the particular stumbling block.

The following table will indicate the quality, the fault, and the remedy which aids the personality to dispel that fault.

Failing	*Herb*	*Virtue*
Restraint	Chicory	Love
Fear	Mimulus..............	Sympathy
Restlessness	Agrimony	Peace
Indecision..........	Scleranthus	Steadfastness
Indifference	Clematis	Gentleness
Weakness...........	Centaury	Strength
Doubt..............	Gentian	Understanding
Over-enthusiasm	Vervain	Tolerance
Ignorance	Cerato..................	Wisdom
Impatience.........	Impatiens	Forgiveness
Terror	Rock Rose	Courage
Grief	Water Violet	Joy

The remedies are endowed with a definite healing power quite apart from faith, neither does their action depend upon the one who administers them, just as a sedative sends a patient to sleep whether given by the nurse or the doctor.

CHAPTER NINE

The real nature of disease.

In true healing the nature and the name of the physical disease is of no consequence whatever. Disease of the body itself is nothing by the result of the disharmony between soul and mind. It is only a symptom of the cause, and as the same cause will manifest itself differently in nearly every individual, seek to remove this cause, and the after results, whatever they may be, will disappear automatically.

We can understand this more clearly by taking as an example the suicide. All suicides do not drown themselves. Some throw themselves from a height, some take poison, but behind it all is despair:

help them to overcome their despair and find someone or something to live for, and they are cured permanently: simply taking away the poison will only save them for the time being, they may later make another attempt. Fear also reacts upon people in quite different ways: some will turn pale, some will flush, some become hysterical and some speechless. Explain the fear to them, show them that they are big enough to overcome and face anything, then nothing can frighten them again. The child will not mind the shadows on the wall if he is given the candle and shown how to make them dance up and down.

We have so long blamed the germ, the weather, the food we eat as the causes of disease; but many of us are immune in an influenza epidemic; many love the exhilaration of a cold wind, and many can eat cheese and drink black coffee late at night with no ill effects. Nothing in nature can hurt us when we are happy and in harmony, on the contrary all nature is there for our use and our enjoyment. It is only when we allow doubt and depression, indecision or fear to creep in that we are sensitive to outside influences.

It is, therefore, the real cause behind the disease, which is of the utmost importance; the mental state of the patient himself, not the condition of his body.

Any disease, however serious, however long-standing, will be cured by restoring to the patient happiness, and desire to carry on with his work in life. Very often it is only some slight alteration in his mode of life, some little fixed idea that is making him intolerant of others, some mistaken sense of responsibility that keeps him in slavery when he might be doing such good work.

There are seven beautiful stages in the healing of disease, these are:

PEACE
HOPE
JOY
FAITH
CERTAINTY
WISDOM
LOVE

CHAPTER TEN

To gain freedom, give freedom.

The ultimate goal of all mankind is perfection, and to gain this state man must learn to pass through all experiences unaffected; he must encounter all interferences and temptations without being deflected from his course: then he is free of all life's difficulties, hardships and sufferings: he has stored up in his soul the perfect love, wisdom, courage, tolerance and understanding that is the result of knowing and seeing everything, for the perfect master is he who has been through every branch of his trade.

We can make this journey a short joyful adventure if we realise that freedom from bondage is only gained by giving freedom; we are set free if we set others others free, for it is only by example we can teach. When we have given freedom to every human being with whom we are in contact; when we have given freedom to every creature, everything around us, then we are free ourselves: when we see that we do not, even in the minutest detail, attempt to dominate, control, or influence the life of another, we shall find that interference has passed out of our own lives, because it is those we bind who bind us. There was a certain young man who was so bound to his possessions that he could not accept a Divine gift.

And we can free ourselves from the domination of others so easily, firstly by giving them absolute freedom, and secondly, by very gently, very lovingly, refusing to be dominated by them. Lord Nelson was very wise in placing his blind eye to the telescope on one occasion. No force, no resentment, no hatred, and no unkindness. Our opponents are our friends, they make the game worth while, and we shall all shake hands at the end of the match.

We must not expect others to do what we want, their ideas are the right ideas for them, and though their pathway may lead in a different direction from ours, the goal at the end of the journey is the same for us all. We do find that it is when we want others to 'fall in with our wishes' that we fall out with them.

We are like cargo-ships bound for the different countries of the world, some for Africa, some for Canada, some for Australia, then returning to the same home port. Why follow another ship to Canada when our destination is Australia? It means such a delay.

Again, we perhaps do not realise what small things may bind us, the very things that we wish to hold are the things that are holding us: it may be a house, a garden, a piece of furniture; even they have their right to freedom. Worldly possessions, after all are transient, they give rise to anxiety and worry because inwardly we know of their inevitable and ultimate loss. They are there to be enjoyed and admired and used to their full capacity, but not to gain so much importance that they become chains to bind us.

If we set everybody and everything around us at liberty, we find that in return we are richer in love and possessions than ever we were before, for the love that gives freedom is the great love that binds the closer.

CHAPTER ELEVEN

Healing.

From time immemorial humanity has recognised that our Creator in His love for us has placed herbs in the field for our healing, just as He has provided the corn and the fruit for our sustenance.

Astrologers, those who have studied the stars, and herbalists, those who have studied the plants, have ever been seeking those remedies which will help us to keep our health and joy.

To find the herb that will help us we must find the object of our life, what we are striving to do, and also understand the difficulties in our path. The difficulties we call faults or failings, but let us not mind these faults and failings, because they are the very proof to us that we are attaining bigger things: our faults should be our encouragements, because they mean that we are aiming high. Let us find for ourselves which of the battles we are particularly fighting, which adversary we are especially trying to overcome, and then take with gratitude and thankfulness that plant which has been sent to help us to victory. We should accept these beautiful herbs of the fields as a sacrament, as our Creator's Divine gift to aid us in our troubles.

In true healing there is no thought whatever of the disease: it is the mental state, the mental difficulty alone, to be considered: it is where we are going wrong in the Divine Plan that matters. This disharmony with our Spiritual Self may produce a hundred different failings in our bodies (for our bodies after all merely reproduce the condition of our minds), but what matters that? If we put our mind right the body will soon be healed. It is as Christ said to us, "Is it easier to say, thy sins be forgiven thee or take up thy bed and walk?"

So again let us clearly understand that our physical illness is of no consequence whatsoever: it is the state of our minds, and that, and that alone, which is of importance. Therefore, ignoring entirely the illness from which we are suffering, we need consider only to which of the following types we belong.

Should any difficulty be found in selecting your own remedy, it will help to ask yourself which of the virtues you most admire in other people; or which of the failings is, in others, your pet aversion, for any fault of which we may still have left a trace and are especially attempting to eradicate, that is the one we most hate to see in other people. It is the way we are encouraged to wipe it out in ourselves.

We are all healers, and with love and sympathy in our natures we are also able to help anyone who really desires health. Seek for the outstanding mental conflict in the patient, give him the remedy that will assist him to overcome that particular fault, and all the encouragement and hope you can, then the healing virtue within him will of itself do all the rest.

CHAPTER TWELVE

The Remedies.

CHICORY

RESTRAINT   LOVE

Are you one of those who long to serve the world: who long to open out both arms and bless all around you; who wish to help and comfort and sympathise, and yet for some reason circumstances or people stop you? Do you find that instead of serving many you are held in the grip of but a few, so that your opportunity of giving as fully as you wish is limited: are you getting to that stage when you wish to realise that it is, "when all men count with you, but none too much?"

Then that beautiful blue Chicory of the cornfields will help you to your freedom, the freedom so necessary to us all before we can serve the world.

MIMULUS

FEAR   SYMPATHY

Are you one of those who are afraid; afraid of people or of circumstances: who go bravely on and yet your life is robbed of joy through
fear; fear of those things that never happen; fear of people who really
have no power over you; fear of tomorrow and what it may bring;
fear of being ill or of losing friends; fear of convention; fear of a
hundred things?

Do you wish to make a stand for your freedom, and yet have not the
courage to break away from your bonds; if so Mimulus, found
growing on the sides of the crystal streams, will set you free to love
your life, and teach you to have the tenderest sympathy for others.

AGRIMONY

RESTLESSNESS   PEACE

Are you one of those who suffer torments; who soul is restless: who
can find no peace, and yet bravely face the world and hide your
torture from your fellow-men: who laugh and smile and jest, and help
those around you to keep a cheery heart whilst you are suffering. Do
you seek to soothe your sorrows by taking wine and drugs to help you
face your trials: do you feel that you must have some stimulant in life
to keep you going?

If so, that beautiful plant Agrimony, growing along the sides of our
lanes and in our meadows, with its church-like spire, and its seeds like
bells, will bring you peace, the peace that 'passeth understanding.'
The lesson of this plant is to enable you to hold peace in the presence
of all trials and difficulties until no one has the power to cause you
irritation.

SCLERANTHUS

INDECISION   STEADFASTNESS

Are you one of those who find it difficult to make decisions; to form
opinions when conflicting thoughts enter your mind so that it is hard
to decide on the right course: when indecision dogs your path and
delays your progress: does first one thing seem right and then
another?

If so you are learning prompt action under trying circumstances; to form correct opinions and be steadfast in following them; and the little green Scleranthus of the cornfields will help you to this end.

CLEMATIS

INDIFFERENCE   GENTLENESS

Are you one of those who find that life has not much interest: who wake almost wishing there were not another day to face: that life is so difficult, so hard, and has so little joy: that nothing really seems worth while, and how good it would be just to go to sleep: that it is scarcely worth the effort to try and get well? Have your eyes that far-away look as though you live in dreams and find the dreams so much more beautiful than life itself: or are your thoughts, perhaps, more often with someone who has passed out of this life? If you feel this way you are learning "to hold on when there is nothing in you except the will which says to you – hold on!" and it is a very great victory to win through.

That beautiful plant which adorns our hedges where there is chalk, the Clematis, better known as Traveller's Joy, and whose feathery seeds are always longing to be blown away and start again, will help you so much to come back and face life and find your work, and bring you joy.

CENTAURY

WEAKNESS   STRENGTH

Are you one of those people whom everybody uses, because in the kindness of your heart you do not like to refuse them anything: do you just give in for the sake of peace rather than do what you know is right, because you do not wish to struggle: whose motive is good, but who are being passively used instead of actively choosing your own work. Those of you who are door-mats are a very long way along the road to being of great service once you can realise that you must be a little more positive in your life.

Centaury, that grows in our pastures, will help you to find your real self, so that you may become an active, positive worker instead of a passive agent.

GENTIAN

DOUBT   UNDERSTANDING

Are you one of those with high ideals, with hopes of doing good; who find yourself discouraged when your ambitions are not quickly realised? When success is in your path are you elated, but when difficulties occur easily depressed?

If so, the little Gentian of our hilly pastures will help you to keep your firmness of purpose, and a happier and more hopeful outlook even when the sky is over-cast. It will bring you encouragement at all times, and the understanding that there is no failure when you are doing your utmost, whatever the apparent result.

VERVAIN

OVER-ENTHUSIASM   TOLERANCE

Are you one of those burning with enthusiasm: longing to do big things, and wishing all done in a moment of time? Do you find it difficult patiently to work out your scheme because you want the result as soon as you start? Do you find your very enthusiasm making you strict with others; wishing them to see things as you see them; trying to force them to your own opinions, and being impatient when they do not follow?

If so, you have within you the power of being a leader and a teacher of men. Vervain, the little mauve flower of the hedge-banks, will help you to the qualities you need, kindness for your brothers, and tolerance for the opinions of others: it will help you to realise that the big things of life are done gently and quietly without strain or stress.

CERATO

IGNORANCE   WISDOM

Are you one of those who feel that you have wisdom; that you could be a philosopher and a guide to your fellow-men? Do you feel the power within you to advise them in their difficulties, to soothe their sorrows, and at all times to be a help to them in their troubles; and yet, through lack of confidence in yourself, you are unable to accomplish this, possibly because you are listening too much to the voice of others and paying too great attention to the conventions of the world?

Do you realise that it is only this lack of confidence in yourself, this ignorance of your own wisdom and knowledge, that tempts you to listen too intently to the advice of others?

Then Cerato will help you to find your individuality, your personality, and, freed from outside influences, enable you to use the great gift of wisdom that you possess for the good of mankind.

IMPATIENS

IMPATIENCE   FORGIVENESS

Are you one of those who know that deep down in your nature there is still a trace of cruelty; when buffeted and harrassed you find it difficult not to have a little malice? Have you still left within you the desire to use force to bring another to your way of thinking: are you impatient and does that impatience sometimes make you cruel: have you left in your nature any trace of the inquisitor?

If so, you are striving for exquisite gentleness and forgiveness, and that beautiful mauve flower, Impatiens, which grows along the sides of some of the Welsh streams, will, with its blessing, help you along the road.

ROCK ROSE

TERROR   COURAGE

Are you one of those in absolute despair, in terror: who feel that you can bear nothing more; terrified as to what will happen: of death; of suicide; of insanity; of some awful disease: or fearful of facing the hopelessness of material circumstances?

If so, you are learning to be brave against great odds, and fighting for your freedom, and the beautiful little yellow Rock Rose, which grows so abundantly on our hilly pastures, will give you the courage to win through.

WATER VIOLET

GRIEF   JOY

Are you one of those great souls who bravely and without complaint, still endeavouring to serve your brother-men, bear suffering calmly and with resignation, not allowing your grief to interfere with your daily work? Have you had real losses, sad times, and yet go quietly on?

If so, the beautiful Water Violet, which floats so freely on the surface of our clearest streams, will help you to understand that you are being purified through your grief, uplifted to a great ideal, so that you may learn to serve your fellow-men even in the hour of your affliction: that you are learning to stand absolutely alone in the world, gaining the intense joy of complete freedom, and therefore of perfect service to mankind. And when this is realised it is no longer sacrifice but the exquisite joy of helpfulness even under all conditions. Moreover that little plant will help you to the understanding that so much you think of in life as being cruel and sad, is truly for the good of those you pity.

We can all take courage and keep a stout heart, for He Who placed us in this world, did so for a great purpose.

He wants us to know that we are His children, to know our own Divinity; to be perfect; to have health and to have happiness. He wants us to know that, through His Love, we can accomplish all things, remembering that it is only when we forget this that we suffer and are unhappy. He wants the life of each one of us to be one of joy and health, and loving service, for as Christ told us:

"My yoke is easy, My burden is light."

Stocks of these remedies can be obtained from the leading London Homœopathic chemists, though they can be prepared as follows by anyone who cares to make their own.

Take a thin glass bowl, fill with clear water from a stream or spring for preference, and float enough of the blooms of the plant to cover the surface. Allow this to stand in bright sunshine until the flowers begin to wilt. Very gently pick out the blooms, pour the water into bottles and add an equal quantity of brandy as a preservative.

One drop alone of this is sufficient to make potent an eight ounce bottle of water, from which doses may be taken by the tea-spoonful as required.

The doses should be taken as the patient feels necessary: hourly in acute cases; three or four times a day in chronic cases until relief occurs when they can be dispensed with.

And may we ever give thanks to God Who, in His Love for us, placed the herbs in the fields for our healing.

– XI –

Ye Suffer From Yourselves

[1931]

An address given at Southport, February, 1931

In coming to address you this evening, I find the task not an easy one.

You are a medical society, and I come to you as a medical man: yet the medicine of which one would speak is so far removed from the orthodox views of today, that there will be little in this paper which savours of the consulting room, nursing home, or hospital ward as we know them at present.

Were it not that you, as followers of Hahnemann, are already vastly in advance of those who preach the teachings of Galen, and the orthodox medicine of the last two thousand years, one would fear to speak at all.

But the teaching of your great Master and his followers has shed so much light upon the nature of disease, and opened up so much of the road which leads to correct healing, that I know you will be prepared to come with me further along that path, and see more of the glories of perfect health, and the true nature of disease and cure.

The inspiration given to Hahnemann brought a light to humanity in the darkness of materialism, when man had come to consider disease as a purely materialistic problem to be relieved and cured by materialistic means alone.

He, like Paracelsus, knew that if our spiritual and mental aspects were in harmony, illness could not exist: and he set out to find remedies which would treat our minds, and thus bring us peace and health.

Hahnemann made a great advance and carried us a long way along the road, but he had only the length of one life in which to work, and it is for us to continue his researches where he left off: to add more to the structure of perfect healing of which he laid the foundation, and so worthily began the building.

The homœopath has already dispensed with much of the unnecessary and unimportant aspects of orthodox medicine, but he has yet further to go. I know that you wish to look forward, for neither the knowledge of the past nor the present is sufficient for the seeker after truth.

Paracelsus and Hahnemann taught us not to pay too much attention to the details of disease, but to treat the personality, the inner man, realising that if our spiritual and mental natures were in harmony disease disappeared. That great foundation to their edifice is the fundamental teaching which must continue.

Hahnemann next saw how to bring about this harmony, and he found that among the drugs and the remedies of the old school, and among elements and plants which he himself selected, he could reverse their action by potentisation, so that the same substance which gave rise to poisonings and symptoms of disease, could – in the minutest quantity – cure those particular symptoms when prepared by his special method.

Thus formulated he the law of "like cures like": another great fundamental principle of life. And he left us to continue the building of the temple, the earlier plans of which had been disclosed to him.

And if we follow on this line of thought, the first great realisation which comes upon us is the truth that it is disease itself which is "like curing like": because disease is the result of wrong activity. It is the natural consequence of disharmony between our bodies and our Souls: it is "like curing like" because it is the very disease itself which hinders and prevents our carrying our wrong actions too far, and at the same time, is a lesson to teach us to correct our ways, and harmonise our lives with the dictates of our Soul.

Disease is the result of wrong thinking and wrong doing, and ceases when the act and thought are put in order. When the lesson of pain and suffering and distress is learnt, there is no further purpose in its presence, and it automatically disappears.

This is what Hahnemann incompletely saw as "like curing like."

COME A LITTLE FURTHER ALONG THE ROAD

Another glorious view then opens out before us, and here we see that true healing can be obtained, not by wrong repelling wrong, but by right replacing wrong: good replacing evil: light replacing darkness.

Here we come to the understanding that we no longer fight disease with disease: no longer oppose illness with the products of illness: no longer attempt to drive out maladies with such substances that can cause them: but, on the contrary, to bring down the opposing virtue which will eliminate the fault.

And the pharmacopœia of the near future should contain only those remedies which have the power to bring down good, eliminating all those whose only quality is to resist evil.

True, hate may be conquered by a greater hate, but it can only be cured by love: cruelty may be prevented by a greater cruelty, but only eliminated when the qualities of sympathy and pity have developed: one fear may be lost and forgotten in the presence of a greater fear, but the real cure of all fear is perfect courage.

And so now, we of this school of medicine have to turn our attention to those beautiful remedies which have been Divinely placed in nature for our healing, amongst those beneficent, exquisite plants and herbs of the countryside.

It is obviously fundamentally wrong to say that "like cures like." Hahnemann had a conception of the truth right enough, but expressed it incompletely. Like may strengthen like, like may repel like, but in the true healing sense like cannot cure like.

If you listen to the teachings of Krishna, Buddha, or Christ, you will find always the teachings of good overcoming evil. Christ taught us not to resist evil, to love our enemies, to bless those who persecute us – there is no like curing like in this. And so in true healing, and so in spiritual advancement, we must always seek good to drive out evil, love to conquer hate, and light to dispel darkness. Thus must we avoid all poisons, all harmful things, and use only the beneficent and beautiful.

No doubt Hahnemann, by his method of potentisation, endeavoured to turn wrong into right, poisons into virtues, but it is simpler to use the beauteous and virtuous remedies direct.

Healing, being above all materialistic things, and materialistic laws, Divine in its origin, is not bound by any of our conventions or ordinary standards. In this we have to raise our ideals, our thoughts, our aspirations, to those glorious and lofty realms taught and shown to us by the Great Masters.

Do not think for one moment that one is detracting from Hahnemann's work, on the contrary, he pointed out the great fundamental laws, the basis; but he had only one life: and had he continued his work longer, no doubt he would have progressed along these lines. We are merely advancing his work, and carrying it to the next natural stage.

Let us now consider why medicine must so inevitably change. The science of the last two thousand years has regarded disease as a material factor which can be eliminated by material means: such, of course, is entirely wrong.

Disease of the body, as we know it, is a result, an end product, a final stage of something much deeper. Disease originates above the physical plane, nearer to the mental. It is entirely the result of a conflict between our spiritual and mortal selves. So long as these two are in harmony, we are in perfect health: but when there is discord, there follows what we know as disease.

Disease is solely and purely corrective: it is neither vindictive nor cruel: but it is the means adopted by our own Souls to point out to us our faults: to prevent our making greater errors: to hinder us from doing more harm: and to bring us back to that path of Truth and Light from which we should never have strayed.

Disease is, in reality, for our good, and is beneficent, though we should avoid it if we had but the correct understanding, combined with the desire to do right.

Whatever errors we make, it re-acts upon ourselves, causing us unhappiness, discomfort, or suffering, according to its nature. The object being to teach us the harmful effect of wrong action or thought: and, by its producing similar results upon ourselves, shows us how it causes distress to others, and is hence contrary to the Great and Divine Law of Love and Unity.

To the understanding physician, the disease itself points out the nature of the conflict. Perhaps this is best illustrated by giving you examples to bring home to you that no matter from what disease you may suffer, it is because there is disharmony between yourself and the Divinity within you, and that you are committing some fault, some error, which your Higher Self is attempting to correct.

Pain is the result of cruelty which causes pain to others, and may be mental or physical: but be sure that if you suffer pain, if you will but search yourselves you will find that some hard action or hard thought is present in your nature: remove this, and your pain will cease. If you suffer from stiffness of joint or limb, you can be equally certain that there is stiffness in your mind; that you are rigidly holding on to some idea, some principle, some convention may be, which you should not have. If you suffer from asthma, or difficulty in breathing, you are in some way stifling another personality; or from lack of courage to do right, smothering yourself. If you waste, it is because you are allowing someone to obstruct your own life-force from entering your body. Even the part of the body affected indicates the nature of the fault. The hand, failure or wrong in action: the foot, failure to assist others: the brain, lack of control: the heart, deficiency or excess, or wrong doing in the aspect of love: the eye, failure to see aright and comprehend the truth when placed before you. And so, exactly, may be worked out the reason and nature of an infirmity: the lesson required of the patient: and the necessary correction to be made.

Let us now glance, for a moment, at the hospital of the future.

It will be a sanctuary of peace, hope and joy. No hurry: no noise: entirely devoid of all the terrifying apparatus and appliances of today: free from the smell of antiseptics and anæsthetics: devoid of everything that suggests illness and suffering. There will be no frequent taking of temperatures to disturb the patient's rest: no daily examinations with stethoscopes and tappings to impress upon the patient's mind the nature of his illness. No constant feeling of the pulse to suggest that the heart is beating too rapidly. For all these things remove the very atmosphere of peace and calm that is so necessary for the patient to bring about his speedy recovery. Neither will there by any need for laboratories; for the minute and microscopic examination of detail will no longer matter when it is fully realised that it is the patient to be treated and not the disease.

The object of all institutions will be to have an atmosphere of peace, and of hope, of joy, and of faith. Everything will be done to encourage the patient to forget his illness; to strive for health; and at the same time to correct any fault in his nature; and come to an understanding of the lesson which he has to learn.

Everything about the hospital of the future will be uplifting and beautiful, so that the patient will seek that refuge, not only to be relieved of his malady, but also to develop the desire to live a life more in harmony with the dictates of his Soul than had been previously done.

The hospital will be the mother of the sick; will take them up in her arms; soothe and comfort them; and bring them hope, faith and courage to overcome their difficulties.

The physician of tomorrow will realise that he of himself has no power to heal, but that if he dedicates his life to the service of his brother-men; to study human nature so that he may, in part, comprehend its meaning; to desire whole-heartedly to relieve suffering, and to surrender all for the help of the sick; then, through him may be sent knowledge to guide them, and the power of healing to relieve their pain. And even then, his power and ability to help will be in proportion to his intensity of desire and his willingness to serve. He will understand that health, like life, is of God, and God alone. That he and the remedies that he uses are merely instruments and agents in the Divine Plan to assist to bring the sufferer back to the path of the Divine Law.

He will have no interest in pathology or morbid anatomy; for his study will be that of health. It will not matter to him whether, for example, shortness of breath is caused by the tubercle baccillus, the streptococcus, or any other organism: but it will matter intensely to know why the patient should have to suffer difficulty of breathing. It will be of no moment to know which of the valves of the heart is damaged, but it will be vital to realise in what way the patient is wrongly developing his love aspect. X-rays will no longer be called into use to examine an arthritic joint, but rather research into the patient's mentality to discover the stiffness in his mind.

The prognosis of disease will no longer depend on physical signs and symptoms, but on the ability of the patient to correct his fault and harmonise himself with his Spiritual Life.

The education of the physician will be a deep study of human nature; a great realisation of the pure and perfect: and an understanding of the Divine state of man: and the knowledge of how to assist those who suffer that they may harmonise their conduct with their Spiritual Self, so that they may bring concord and health to the personality.

He will have to be able, from the life and history of the patient, to understand the conflict which is causing disease or disharmony between the body and Soul, and thus enable him to give the necessary advice and treatment for the relief of the sufferer.

He will also have to study Nature and Nature's Laws: be conversant with Her Healing Powers, that he may utilise these for the benefit and advantage of the patient.

The treatment of tomorrow will be essentially to bring four qualities to the patient.

First, peace: secondly, hope: thirdly, joy: and fourthly, faith.

And all the surroundings and attention will be to that end. To surround the patient with such an atmosphere of health and light as will encourage recovery. At the same time, the errors of the patient, having been diagnosed, will be pointed out, and assistance and encouragement given that they may be conquered.

In addition to this, those beautiful remedies, which have been Divinely enriched with healing powers, will be administered, to open up those channels to limit more ot the light of the Soul, that the patient may be flooded with healing virtue.

The action of these remedies is to raise our vibrations and open up our channels for the reception of our Spiritual Self, to flood our natures with the particular virtue we need, and wash out from us the fault which is causing harm. They are able, like beautiful music, or any gloriously uplifting thing which gives us inspiration, to raise our very natures, and bring us nearer to our Souls: and by that very act, to bring us peace, and relieve our sufferings.

They cure, not by attacking disease, but by flooding our bodies with the beautiful vibrations of our Higher Nature, in the presence of which disease melts as snow in the sunshine.

And, finally, how they must change the attitude of the patient towards disease and health.

Gone forever must be the thought that relief may be obtained by the payment of gold or silver. Health, like life, is of Divine origin, and can only be obtained by Divine Means. Money, luxury, travel, may outwardly appear to be able to purchase for us an improvement in our physical being: but these things can never give us true health.

The patient of tomorrow must understand that he, and he alone, can bring himself relief from suffering, though he may obtain advice and help from an elder brother who will assist him in his effort.

Health exists when there is perfect harmony between Soul and mind and body: and this harmony, and this harmony alone, must be attained before cure can be accomplished.

In the future there will no pride in being ill: on the contrary, people will be as ashamed of sickness as they should be of crime.

And now I want to explain to you two conditions which are probably giving rise to more disease in this country than any other single cause: the great failings of our civilisation – greed and idolatry.

Disease, is, of course, sent to us as a correction. We bring it entirely upon ourselves: it is the result of our own wrong doing and wrong thinking. Can we but correct our faults and live in harmony with the Divine Plan, illness can never assail us.

In this, our civilisation, greed overshadows all. There is greed for wealth, for rank, for position, for worldly honours, for comfort, for popularity: yet it is not of these one would speak, because even they are, in comparison, harmless.

The worst of all is the greed to possess another individual. True, this is so common amongst us that it has come to be looked upon as almost right and proper: yet that does not mitigate the evil: for, to desire possession or influence over another individual or personality, is to usurp the power of our Creator.

How many folk can you number amongst your friends or relations who are free? How many are there who are not bound or influenced or controlled by some other human being? How many are there who could say, that day by day, month by month, and year by year, "I obey only the dictates of my Soul, unmoved by the influence of other people?"

And yet, everyone of us is a free Soul, answerable only to God for our actions, aye, even our very thoughts.

Possibly the greatest lesson of life is to learn freedom. Freedom from circumstance, environment, other personalities, and most of all from ourselves: because until we are free we are unable fully to give and to serve our brother-men.

Remember that whether we suffer disease or hardship: whether we are surrounded by relations or friends who may annoy us: whether we have to live amongst those who rule and dictate to us, who interfere with our plans and hamper our progress, it is of our own making: it is because there is still within us a trace left to bar the freedom of someone: or the absence of courage to claim our own individuality, our birthright.

The moment that we ourselves have given complete liberty to all around us: when we no longer desire to bind and limit: when we no longer expect anything from anyone: when our only thought is to give and give and never to take, that moment shall we find that we are free of all the world: our bonds will fall from us: our chains be broken: and for the first time in our lives shall we know the exquisite joy of perfect liberty. Freed from all human restraint, the willing and joyous servant of our Higher Self alone.

So greatly has the possessive power developed in the West that it is necessitating great disease before people will recognize the error and correct their ways: and according to the severity and type of or domination over another, so must we suffer as long as we continue to usurp a power which does not belong to man.

Absolute freedom is our birthright, and this we can only obtain when we grant that liberty to every living Soul who may come into our lives. For truly we reap as we sow, and truly "as we mete so it shall be measured out to us."

Exactly as we thwart another life, be it young or old, so must that re-act upon ourselves. If we limit their activities, we may find our bodies limited with stiffness: if, in addition, we cause them pain and suffering, we must be prepared to bear the same, until we have made amends: and there is no disease, even however severe, that may not be needed to check our actions and alter our ways.

To those of you who suffer at the hands of another, take courage; for it means that you have reached that stage of advancement when you are being taught to gain your freedom: and the very pain and suffering which you are bearing is teaching you how to correct your own fault, and as soon as you have realised the fault and put that right, your troubles are over.

The way to set about to do this work is to practise exquisite gentleness: never by thought or word or deed to hurt another. Remember that all people are working out their own salvation; are going through life to learn those lessons for the perfection of their own Soul; and that they must do it for themselves: that they must gain their own experiences: learn the pitfalls of the world, and, of their own effort, find the pathway which leads to the mountain top. The most that we can do is, when we have a little more knowledge and experience than a younger brother, very gently to guide them. If they will listen, well and good: if not, we must patiently wait until they have had further experience to teach them their fault, and then they may come to us again.

We should strive to be so gentle, so quiet, so patiently helpful that we move among our fellow men more as a breath of air or a ray of sunshine: ever ready to help them when they ask: but never forcing them to our own views.

And I want now to tell you of another great hindrance to health, which is very, very common today, and one of the greatest obstacles that physicians encounter in their endeavour to heal. An obstacle which is a form of idolatry. Christ said "Ye cannot serve God and mammon," and yet the service of mammon is one of our greatest stumbling blocks.

There was an angel once, a glorious, magnificent angel, that appeared to St John, and St John fell in adoration and worshipped. But the angel said to him, "See thou do it not, I am thy fellow servant and of thy brethren. Worship God." And yet today, tens of thousands of us worship not God, not even a mighty angel, but a fellow human being. I can assure you that one of the greatest difficulties which has to be overcome is a sufferer's worship of another mortal.

How common is the expression: "I must ask my father, my sister, my husband." What a tragedy. To think that a human Soul, developing his Divine evolution, should stop to ask permission of a fellow-traveller. To whom does he imagine that he owes his origin, his being, his life – to a fellow-traveller or to his Creator?

We must understand that we are answerable for our actions, and for our thoughts to God, and to God alone. And that to be influenced, to obey the wishes, or consider the desires of another mortal is idolatry indeed. Its penalty is severe, it binds us with chains, it places us in prisons, it confines our very life; and so it should, and so we justly deserve, if we listen to the dictates of a human being, when our whole self should know but one command – that of our Creator, Who gave us our life and our understanding.

Be certain that the individual who considers above his duty his wife, his child, his father, or his friend, is an idolator, serving mammon and not God.

Remember the words of Christ, "Who is My mother, and who are My brethren," which imply that even all of us, small and insignificant as we may be, are here to serve our brother-men, humanity, the world at large, and never, for the briefest moment, to be under the dictates and commands of another human individual against those motives which we know to be our Soul's commands.

Be captains of your Souls, be masters of your fate (which means let your selves be ruled and guided entirely, without let or hindrance from person or circumstance, by the Divinity within you), ever living in accordance with the laws of, and answerable only to the God Who gave you your life.

And yet, one more point to bring before your notice. Ever remember the injunction which Christ gave to His disciples, "Resist not evil." Sickness and wrong are not to be conquered by direct fighting, but by replacing them by good. Darkness is removed by light, not by greater darkness: hate by love: cruelty by sympathy and pity: and disease by health.

Our whole object is to realise our faults, and endeavour so to develop the opposing virtue that the fault will disappear from us like snow melts in the sunshine. Don't fight your worries: don't struggle with your disease: don't grapple with your infirmities: rather forget them in concentrating on the development of the virtue you require.

And so now, in summing up, we can see the mighty part that homœopathy is going to play in the conquest of disease in the future.

Now that we have come to the understanding that disease itself is "like curing like": that it is of our own making: for our correction and for our ultimate good: and that we can avoid it, if we will but learn the lessons needed, and correct our faults before the severer lesson of suffering is necessary. This is the natural continuation of Hahnemann's great work; the consequence of that line of thought which was disclosed to him, leading us a step further towards perfect understanding of disease and health, and is the stage to bridge the gap between where he left us and the dawn of that day when humanity will have reached that state of advancement when it can receive direct the glory of Divine Healing.

The understanding physician, selecting well his remedies from the beneficent plants in nature, those Divinely enriched and blessed, will be enabled to assist his patients to open up those channels which allow greater communion between Soul and body, and thus the development of the virtues needed to wipe away the faults. This brings to mankind the hope of real health combined with mental and spiritual advance.

For the patients, it will be necessary that they are prepared to face the truth, that disease is entirely and only due to faults within themselves, just as the wages of sin is death. They will have to have the desire to correct those faults, to live a better and more useful life, and to realise that healing depends on their own effort, though they may go to the physician for guidance and assistance in their trouble.

Health can be no more obtained by payment of gold than a child can purchase his education: no sum of money can teach the pupil to write, he must learn of himself, guided by an experienced teacher. And so it is with health.

There are the two great commandments: "Love God and thy neighbour." Let us develop our individuality that we may obtain complete freedom to serve the Divinity within ourselves, and that Divinity alone: and give unto all others their absolute freedom, and serve them as much as lies within our power, according to the dictates of our Souls, ever remembering that as our own liberty increases, so grows our freedom and ability to serve our fellow-men.

Thus we have to face the fact that disease is entirely of our own making and that the only cure is to correct our faults. All true healing aims at assisting the patient to put his Soul and mind and body in harmony. This can only be done by himself, though advice and help by an expert brother may greatly assist him.

As Hahnemann laid down, all healing which is not from within, is harmful, and apparent cure of the body obtained through materialistic methods, obtained only through the action of others, without self-help, may certainly bring physical relief, but harm to our Higher Natures, for the lesson has remained unlearnt, and the fault has not been eradicated.

It is terrible today to think of the amount of artificial and superficial cures obtained through money and wrong methods in medicine; wrong methods because they merely suppress symptoms, give apparent relief, without removing the cause.

Healing must come from within ourselves, by acknowledging and correcting our faults, and harmonising our being with the Divine Plan. And as the Creator, in His mercy, has placed certain Divinely enriched herbs to assist us to our victory, let us seek out these and use them to the best of our ability, to help us climb the mountain of our evolution, until the day when we shall reach the summit of perfection.

Hahnemann had realised the truth of "like curing like," which is in reality disease curing wrong action: that true healing is one stage higher than this: love and all its attributes driving out wrong.

That in correct healing nothing must be used which relieves the patient of his own responsibility: but such means only must be adopted which help him to overcome his faults.

That we now know that certain remedies in the homœopathic pharmacopœia have the power to elevate our vibrations, thus bringing more union between our mortal and Spiritual self, and effecting the cure by greater harmony thus produced.

And finally, that it is our work to purify the pharmacopœia, and to add to it new remedies until it contains only those which are beneficent and uplifting.

— XII —

Heal Thyself

[Published C.W. Daniel Co. 1931]

*An Explanation of the Real
Cause and Cure of Disease*

*This book is dedicated
to
all who suffer
or
who are in distress*

CHAPTER ONE

It is not the object of this book to suggest that the art of healing is unnecessary, far be from it any such intention; but it is humbly hoped that it will be a guide to those who suffer to seek within themselves the real origin of their maladies, so that they may assist themselves in their own healing. Moreover, it is hoped that it may stimulate those, both in the medical profession and in religious orders, who have the welfare of humanity at heart, to redouble their efforts in seeking the relief of human suffering, and so hasten that day when the victory over disease will be complete.

The main reason for the failure of modern medical science is that it is dealing with results and not causes. For many centuries the real nature of disease has been masked by materialism, and thus disease itself has been given every opportunity of extending its ravages, since it has not been attacked at its origin. The situation is like to an enemy strongly fortified in the hills, continually waging guerilla warfare in the country around, while the people, ignoring the fortified garrison, content themselves with repairing the damaged houses and burying the dead, which are the result of the raids of the marauders. So, generally speaking, is the situation in medicine today; nothing more than the patching up of those attacked and the burying of those who are slain, without a thought being given to the real stronghold.

Disease will never be cured or eradicated by present materialistic methods, for the simple reason that disease in its origin is not material. What we know as disease is an ultimate result produced in the body, the end product of deep and long acting forces, and even if material treatment alone is apparently successful this is nothing more than a temporary relief unless the real cause has been removed. The modern trend of medical science, by misinterpreting the true nature of disease and concentrating it in materialistic terms in the physical body, has enormously increased its power, firstly, by distracting the thoughts of people from its true origin and hence from the effective method of attack, and secondly, by localising it in the body, thus obscuring true hope of recovery and raising a mighty disease complex of fear, which never should have existed.

Disease is in essence the result of conflict between Soul and Mind, and will never be eradicated except by spiritual and mental effort. Such efforts, if properly made with understanding, as we shall see later, can cure and prevent disease by removing those basic factors which are its primary cause. No effort directed to the body alone can do more than superficially repair damage, and in this there is no cure, since the cause is still operative and may at any moment again demonstrate its presence in another form. In fact, in many cases apparent recovery is harmful, since it hides from the patient the true cause of his trouble, and in the satisfaction of apparently renewed health the real factor, being unnoticed, may gain in strength. Contrast these cases with that of the patient who knows, or who is by some wise physician instructed in, the nature of the adverse spiritual or mental forces at work, the result of which has precipitated what we call disease in the physical body. If that patient directly attempts to neutralise those forces, health improves as soon as this is successfully begun, and when it is completed the disease will disappear. This is true healing by attacking the stronghold, the very base of the cause of suffering.

One of the exceptions to materialistic methods in modern medical science is that of the great Hahnemann, the founder of Homœopathy, who with his realisation of the beneficent love of the Creator and of the Divinity which resides within man, by studying the mental attitude of his patients towards life, environment and their respective diseases, sought to find in the herbs of the field and in the realms of nature the remedy which would not only heal their bodies but would at the same time uplift their mental outlook. May his science be extended and developed by those true physicians who have the love of humanity at heart.

Five hundred years before Christ some physicians of ancient India, working under the influence of Lord Buddha, advanced the art of healing to so perfect a state that they were able to abolish surgery, although the surgery of their time was as efficient, or more so, than that of the present day. Such men as Hippocrates with his mighty ideals of healing, Paracelsus with his certainty of the divinity in man, and Hahnemann who realised that disease originated in a plane above the physical – all these knew much of the real nature and remedy of suffering. What untold misery would have been spared during the last twenty or twenty-five centuries had the teaching of these great masters of their art been followed, but, as in other things, materialism has appealed too strongly to the Western world, and for so long a time, that the voices of the practical obstructors have risen above the advice of those who knew the truth.

Let it here be briefly stated that disease, though apparently so cruel, is in itself beneficent and for our good and, if rightly interpreted, it will guide us to our essential faults. If properly treated, it will be the cause of the removal of those faults and leave us better and greater than before. Suffering is a corrective to point out a lesson which by other means we have failed to grasp, and never can it be eradicated until that lesson is learnt. Let is also be known that in those who understand and are able to read the significance of premonitory symptoms disease may be prevented before its onset or aborted in its earlier stages if the proper corrective spiritual and mental efforts be undertaken. Nor need any case despair, however severe, for the fact that the individual is still granted physical life indicates that the Soul who rules is not without hope.

CHAPTER TWO

To understand the nature of disease certain fundamental truths have to be acknowledged.

The first of these is that man has a Soul which is his real self; a Divine, Mighty Being, a Son of the Creator of all things, of which the body, although the earthly temple of that Soul, is but the minutest reflection: that our Soul, our Divinity Who resides in and around us, lays down for us our lives as He wishes them to be ordered and, so far as we will allow, ever guides, protects and encourages us, watchful and beneficent to lead us always for our utmost advantage: that He, our Higher Self, being a spark of the Almighty, is thereby invincible and immortal.

The second principle is that we, as we know ourselves in this world, are personalities down here for the purpose of gaining all the knowledge and experience which can be obtained through earthly existence, of developing virtues which we lack and of wiping out all that is wrong within us, thus advancing towards the perfection of our natures. The Soul knows what environment and what circumstances will best enable us to do this, and hence He places us in that branch of life most suited for that object.

Thirdly, we must realise that the short passage on this earth, which we know as life, is but a moment in the course of our evolution, as one day at school is to a life, and although we can for the present only see and comprehend that one day, our intuition tells us that birth was infinitely far from our beginning and death infinitely far from our ending. Our Souls, which are really we, are immortal, and the bodies of which we are conscious and temporary, merely as horses we ride to go a journey, or instruments we use to do a piece of work.

Then follows a fourth great principle, that so long as our Souls and personalities are in harmony all is joy and peace, happiness and health. It is when our personalities are led astray from the path laid down by the Soul, either by our own worldly desires or by the persuasion of others, that a conflict arises. This conflict is the root cause of disease and unhappiness. No matter what our work in the world – bootblack or monarch, landlord or peasant, rich or poor – so long as we do that particular work according to the dictates of the Soul, all is well; and we can further rest assured that in whatever station of life we are placed, princely or lowly, it contains the lessons and experiences necessary at the moment for our evolution, and gives us the best advantage for the development of ourselves.

The next great principle is the understanding of the Unity of all things: that the Creator of all things is Love, and that everything of which we are conscious is in all its infinite number of forms a manifestation of that Love, whether it be a planet or a pebble, a star or a dewdrop, man or the lowest form of life. It may be possible to get a glimpse of this conception by thinking of our Creator as a great blazing sun of beneficence and love and from the centre an infinite number of beams radiate in every direction, and that we and all of which we are conscious are particles at the end of those beams, sent out to gain experience and knowledge, but ultimately to return to the great centre. And though to us each ray may appear separate and distinct, it is in reality part of the great central Sun. Separation is impossible, for as soon as a beam of light is cut off from its source it ceases to exist. Thus we may comprehend a little of the impossibility of separateness, as although each ray may have its individuality, it is nevertheless part of the great central creative power. Thus any action against ourselves or against another affects the whole, because by causing imperfection in a part it reflects on the whole, every particle of which must ultimately become perfect.

So we see there are two great possible fundamental errors: dissociation between our Souls and our personalities, and cruelty or wrong to others, for this is a sin against Unity. Either of these brings conflict, which leads to disease. An understanding of where we are making an error (which is so often not realised by us) and an earnest endeavour to correct the fault will lead not only to a life of joy and peace, but also to health.

Disease is in itself beneficent, and has for its object the bringing back of the personality to the Divine will of the Soul; and thus we can see that it is both preventable and avoidable, since if we could only realise for ourselves the mistakes we are making and correct these by spiritual and mental means there would be no need for the severe lesson of suffering. Every opportunity is given us by the Divine Power to mend our ways before, as a last resort, pain and suffering have to be applied. It may not be the errors of this life, this day at school, which we are combating; and although we in our physical minds may not be conscious of the reason of our suffering, which may to us appear cruel and without reason, yet our Souls (which are ourselves) know the full purpose and are guiding us to our best advantage. Nevertheless, understanding and correction of our errors would shorten our illness and bring us back to health. Knowledge of the Soul's purpose and acquiescence in that knowledge means the relief of earthly suffering and distress, and leaves us free to develop our evolution in joy and happiness.

There are two great errors: first, to fail to honour and obey the dictates of our Soul, and second, to act against Unity. On account of the former, be ever reluctant to judge others, because what is right for one is wrong for another. The merchant, whose work it is to build up a big trade not only to his own advantage but also to that of all those whom he may employ, thereby gaining knowledge of efficiency and control and developing the virtues associated with each, must of necessity use different qualities and different virtues from those of a nurse, sacrificing her life in the care of the sick; and yet both, if obeying the dictates of their Souls, are rightly learning those qualities necessary for their evolution. It is obeying the commands of our Soul, our Higher Self, which we learn through conscience, instinct and intuition, that matters.

Thus we see that by its very principles and in its very essence, disease is both preventable and curable, and it is the work of spiritual healers and physicians to give, in addition to material remedies, the knowledge to the suffering of the error of their lives, and of the manner in which these errors can be eradicated, and so to lead the sick back to health and joy.

CHAPTER THREE

What we know as disease is the terminal stage of a much deeper disorder, and to ensure complete success in treatment it is obvious that dealing with the final result alone will not be wholly effective unless the basic cause is also removed. There is one primary error which man can make, and that is action against Unity; this originates in self-love. So also we may say that there is but one primary affliction – discomfort, or disease. And as action against Unity may be divided into various types, so also may disease – the result of these actions – be separated into main groups, corresponding to their causes. The very nature of an illness will be a useful guide to assist in discovering the type of action which is being taken against the Divine Law of Love and Unity.

If we have in our nature sufficient love of all things, then we can do no harm; because that love would stay our hand in any action, our mind at any thought which might hurt another. But we have not yet reached that state of perfection; if we had, there would be no need for our existence here. But all of us are seeking and advancing towards that state, and those of us who suffer in mind or body are by this very suffering being led towards that ideal condition; and if we will but read it aright, we may not only hasten our steps towards that goal, but also save ourselves illness and distress. From the moment the lesson is understood and the error eliminated there is no longer need for the correction, because we must remember that suffering is in itself beneficent, in that it points out to us when we are taking wrong paths and hastens our evolution to its glorious perfection.

The real primary diseases of man are such defects as pride, cruelty, hate, self-love, ignorance, instability and greed; and each of these, if considered, will be found to be adverse to Unity. Such defects as these are the real diseases (using the word in the modern sense), and it is a continuation and persistence in such defects after we have reached that stage of development when we know them to be wrong, which precipitates in the body the injurious results which we know as illness.

Pride is due, firstly, to lack of recognition of the smallness of the personality and its utter dependence on the Soul, and that all the successes it may have are not of itself but are blessings bestowed by the Divinity within; secondly, to loss of the sense of proportion, of the minuteness of one amidst the scheme of Creation. As Pride invariably refuses to bend with humility and resignation to the Will of the Great Creator, it commits actions contrary to that Will.

Cruelty is a denial of the unity of all and a failure to understand that any action adverse to another is in opposition to the whole, and hence an action against Unity. No man would practise its injurious effects against those near and dear to him, and by the law of Unity we have to grow until we understand that everyone, as being part of a whole, must become near and dear to us, until even those who persecute us call up only feelings of love and sympathy.

Hate is the opposite of Love, the reverse of the Law of Creation. It is contrary to the whole Divine scheme and is a denial of the Creator; it leads only to such actions and thoughts which are adverse to Unity and the opposite of those which would be dictated by Love.

Self-love again is a denial of Unity and the duty we owe to our brother men by putting the interests of ourselves before the good of humanity and the care and protection of those immediately around us.

Ignorance is the failure to learn, the refusal to see Truth when the opportunity is offered, and leads to many wrong acts such as can only exist in darkness and are not possible when the light of Truth and Knowledge is around us.

Instability, indecision and weakness of purpose result when the personality refuses to be ruled by the Higher Self, and lead us to betray others through our weakness. Such a condition would not be possible had we within us the knowledge of the Unconquerable, Invincible Divinity which is in reality ourselves.

Greed leads to a desire for power. It is a denial of the freedom and individuality of every soul. Instead of recognising that everyone of us is down here to develop freely upon his own lines according to the dictates of the soul alone, to increase his individuality, and to work free and unhampered, the personality with greed desires to dictate, mould and command, usurping the power of the Creator.

Such are examples of real disease, the origin and basis of all our suffering and distress. Each of such defects, if persisted in against the voice of the Higher Self, will produce a conflict which must of necessity be reflected in the physical body, producing its own specific type of malady.

We can now see how any type of illness from which we may suffer will guide us to the discovery of the fault which lies behind our affliction. For example, Pride, which is arrogance and rigidity of mind, will give rise to those diseases which produce rigidity and stiffness of the body. Pain is the result of cruelty, whereby the patient learns through personal suffering not to inflict it upon others, either from a physical or from a mental standpoint. The penalties of Hate are loneliness, violent uncontrollable temper, mental nerve storms and conditions of hysteria. The diseases of introspection – neurosis, neurasthenia and similar conditions – which rob life of so much enjoyment, are caused by excessive Self-love. Ignorance and lack of wisdom bring their own difficulties in everyday life, and in addition should there be a persistence in refusing to see truth when the opportunity has been given, short-sightedness and impairment of vision and hearing are the natural consequences. Instability of mind must lead to the same quality in the body with those various disorders which affect movement and co-ordination. The result of greed and domination of others is such diseases as will render the sufferer a slave to his own body, with desires and ambitions curbed by the malady.

Moreover, the very part of the body affected is no accident, but is in accordance with the law of cause and effect, and again will be a guide to help us. For example, the heart, the fountain of life and hence of love, is attacked when especially the love side of the nature towards humanity is not developed or is wrongly used; a hand affected denotes failure or wrong in action; the brain being the centre of control, if afflicted, indicates lack of control in the personality. Such must follow as the law lays down. We are all ready to admit the many results which may follow a fit of violent temper, the shock of sudden bad news; if trivial affairs can thus affect the body, how much more serious and deep-rooted must be a prolonged conflict between soul and body. Can we wonder that the result gives rise to such grievous complaints as the diseases amongst us today?

But yet there is no cause for depression. The prevention and cure of disease can be found by discovering the wrong within ourselves and eradicating this fault by the earnest development of the virtue which will destroy it; not by fighting the wrong, but by bringing in such a flood of its opposing virtue that it will be swept from our natures.

CHAPTER FOUR

So we find that there is nothing of the nature of accident as regards disease, either in its type or in that part of the body which is affected; like all other results of energy it follows the law of cause and effect. Certain maladies may be caused by direct physical means, such as those associated with some poisons, accidents and injuries, and gross excesses; but disease in general is due to some basic error in our constitution, as in the examples already given.

And thus for a complete cure not only must physical means be used, choosing always the best methods which are known to the art of healing, but we ourselves must also endeavour to the utmost of our ability to remove any fault in our nature; because final and complete healing ultimately comes from within, from the Soul itself, which by His beneficence radiates harmony throughout the personality, when allowed to do so.

As there is one great root cause of all disease, namely self-love, so there is one great certain method of relief of all suffering, the conversion of self-love into devotion to others. If we but sufficiently develop the quality of losing ourselves in the love and care of those around us, enjoying the glorious adventure of gaining knowledge and helping others, our personal griefs and sufferings rapidly come to an end. It is the great ultimate aim: the losing of our own interests in the service of humanity. It matters not the station in life in which our Divinity has placed us. Whether engaged in trade or profession, rich or poor, monarch or beggar, for one and all it is possible to carry on the work of their respective vocations and yet be veritable blessings to those around by communicating to them the Divine Love of Brotherhood.

But the vast majority of us have some way to travel before we can reach this state of perfection, although it is surprising how rapidly any individual may advance along these lines if the effort is seriously made, providing he trusts not in his poor personality alone but has implicit faith, that by the example and teaching of the great masters of the world he may be enabled to unite himself with his own Soul, the Divinity within, when all things become possible. In most of us there is one, or more, adverse defect which is particularly hindering our advancement, and it is such defect, or defects, which we must especially seek out within ourselves, and whilst striving to develop and extend the love side of our nature towards the world, endeavour at the same time to wash away any such defect in particular by the flooding of our nature with the opposing virtue. At first this may be a little difficult, but only just at first, for it is remarkable how rapidly a truly encouraged virtue will increase, linked with the knowledge that with the aid of the Divinity within us, if we but persevere, failure is impossible.

In the development of Universal Love within ourselves, we must learn to realise more and more that every human being, however lowly, is a son of the Creator, and that one day and in due time he will advance to perfection just as we all hope to do. However base a man or creature may appear, we must remember that there is the Divine Spark within, which will slowly but surely grow until the glory of the Creator irradiates that being.

Moreover, the question of right or wrong, of good and evil, is purely relative. That which is right in the natural evolution of the aboriginal would be wrong for the more enlightened of our civilisation, and that which might even be a virtue in such as ourselves might be out of place, and hence wrong, in one who has reached the stage of discipleship. What we call wrong or evil is in reality good out of place, and hence is purely relative. Let us remember also that our standard of idealism again is relative; to the animals we must appear as veritable gods, whereas we in ourselves are very far below the standards of the great White Brotherhood of Saints and Martyrs who have given their all to be examples to us. Hence we must have compassion and sympathy for the lowliest, for whilst we may consider ourselves as having advanced far above their level, we are in ourselves minute indeed, and have yet a long journey before us to reach the standard of our older brothers, whose light shines throughout the world in every age.

If Pride assails us, let us try to realise that our personalities are in themselves as nothing, unable to do any good work or acceptable service, or to resist the powers of darkness, unless assisted by that Light which is from above, the Light of our Soul; endeavour to comprehend a glimpse of the omnipotence and unthinkable mightiness of our Creator, Who makes in all perfection a world in one drop of water and systems upon systems of universes, and try to realise the relative humility we owe and our utter dependence upon Him. We learn to pay homage and give respect to our human superiors; how infinitely more should we acknowledge our own frailty with utmost humility before the Great Architect of the Universe!

If Cruelty, or Hate, bar our way to progress, let us remember that Love is the foundation of Creation, that in every living soul there is some good, and that in the best of us there is some bad. By seeking the good in others, even in those who at first offend us, we shall learn to develop, if nothing more, some sympathy and a hope that they will see better ways; then it follows that the desire will arise to help them to that uplift. The ultimate conquest of all will be through love and gentleness, and when we have sufficiently developed these two qualities nothing will be able to assail us, since we shall ever have compassion and not offer resistance; for again by the same law of cause and effect it is resistance which damages. Our object in life is to follow the dictates of our Higher Self, undeterred by the influence of others, and this can only be achieved if we gently go our own way, but at the same time never interfere with the personality of another or cause the least harm by any method of cruelty or hate. We must strive to learn love of others, beginning perhaps with one individual or even an animal, and let this love develop and extend over a wider and wider range, until its opposing defects will automatically disappear. Love begets Love, as Hate does Hate.

The cure of self-love is effected by the turning outwards to others of the care and attention which we are devoting to ourselves, becoming so engrossed in their welfare that we forget ourselves in that endeavour. As one great order of Brotherhood expresses it, "to seek the solace of own distress by extending relief and consolation to our fellow creatures in the hour of their affliction," and there is no surer way of curing self-love and the disorders which follow it than by such a method.

Instability can be eradicated by the development of self-determination, by making up the mind and doing things with definiteness instead of wavering and hovering. Even if at first we may sometimes make errors, it were better to act than to let opportunities pass for the want of decision. Determination will soon grow; fear of plunging into life will disappear, and the experiences gained will guide our mind to better judgement.

To eradicate Ignorance, again let us not be afraid of experience, but with mind awake and with eyes and ears wide open take in every particle of knowledge which may be obtained. At the same time we must keep flexible in thought, lest preconceived ideas and former convictions rob us of the opportunity of gaining fresh and wider knowledge. We should be ever ready to expand the mind and to disregard any idea, however firmly rooted, if under wider experience a greater truth shows itself.

Like Pride, Greed is a great obstacle to advancement, and both of these must be ruthlessly washed away. The results of Greed are serious indeed, because it leads us to interfere with the soul-development of our fellow-men. We must realise that every being is here to develop his own evolution according to the dictates of his Soul, and his Soul alone, and that none of us must do anything but encourage our brother in that development. We must help him to hope and, if in our power, increase his knowledge and worldly opportunities to gain his advancement. Just as we would wish others to help us up the steep and difficult mountain path of life so let us be ever ready to lend a helping hand and give the experience of our wider knowledge to a weaker or younger brother. Such should be the attitude of parent to child, master to man or comrade to comrade, giving care, love and protection as far as may be needed and beneficial, yet never for one moment interfering with the natural evolution of the personality, as this must be dictated by the Soul.

Many of us in our childhood and early life are much nearer to our own Soul than we are in later years, and have then clearer ideas of our work in life, the endeavours we are expected to make and the character we are required to develop. The reason for this is that the materialism and circumstances of our age, and the personalities with whom we associate, lead us away from the voice of our Higher Self and bind us firmly to the commonplace with its lack of ideals, all too evident in this civilisation. Let the parent, the master and the comrade ever strive to encourage the growth of the Higher Self within those over whom they have the wonderful privilege and opportunity to exert their influence, but let them ever allow freedom to others, as they hope to have freedom given to them.

So in a similar way may we seek out any faults in our constitution and wash them out by developing the opposing virtue, thus removing from our nature the cause of the conflict between Soul and personality, which is the primary basic cause of disease. Such action alone, if the patient has faith and strength, will bring relief, health and joy, and in those not so strong will materially assist the work of the earthly physician in bringing about the same result.

We must earnestly learn to develop individuality according to the dictates of our own Soul, to fear no man and to see that no one interferes with, or dissuades us from, the development of our evolution, the fulfilment of our duty and the rendering of help to our fellow-men, remembering that the further we advance, the greater blessing we become to those around. Especially must we be on guard in the giving of help to other people, no matter whom they be, to be certain that the desire to help comes from the dictates of the Inner Self and is not a false sense of duty imposed by the suggestion or persuasion of a more dominant personality. One tragedy resulting from modern convention is of such a type, and it is impossible to calculate the thousands of hindered lives, the myriads of missed opportunities, the sorrow and the suffering so caused, the countless number of children who from a sense of duty have perhaps for years waited upon an invalid parent when the only malady the parent has known has been greed of attention. Think of the armies of men and women who have been prevented from doing perhaps some great and useful work for humanity because their personality has been captured by some one individual from whom they have not had the courage to win freedom; the children who in their early days know and desire their ordained calling, and yet from difficulties of circumstance, dissuasion by others and weakness of purpose glide into some other branch of life, where they are neither happy nor able to develop their evolution as they might otherwise have done. It is the dictates of our conscience alone which can tell us whether our duty lies with one or many, how and whom we should serve; but whichever it may be, we should obey that command to the utmost of our ability.

Finally, let us not fear to plunge into life; we are here to gain experience and knowledge, and we shall learn but little unless we face realities and seek to our utmost. Such experience can be gained in every quarter, and the truths of nature and of humanity can be won just as effectively, perhaps even more so, in a country cottage as amongst the noise and hustle of a city.

CHAPTER FIVE

As lack of individuality (that is, the allowing of interference with the personality, such interference preventing it from complying with the demands of the Higher Self) is of such great importance in the production of disease, and as it often begins early in life, let us now consider the true relation between parent and child, teacher and pupil.

Fundamentally, the office of parenthood is to be the privileged means (and, indeed, it should be considered as divinely privileged) of enabling a soul to contact this world for the sake of evolution. If properly understood, there is probably no greater opportunity offered to mankind than this, to be the agent of the physical birth of a soul and to have the care of the young personality during the first few years of its existence on earth. The whole attitude of parents should be to give the little newcomer all the spiritual, mental and physical guidance to the utmost of their ability, ever remembering that the wee one is an individual soul come down to gain his own experience and knowledge in this own way according to the dictates of his Higher Self, and every possible freedom should be given for unhampered development.

The office of parenthood is one of divine service, and should be respected as much as, or perhaps even more than, any other duty we may be called upon to undertake. As it is one of sacrifice, it must ever be borne in mind that nothing whatever should be required in return from the child, the whole object being to give, and give alone, gentle love, protection and guidance until the soul takes charge of the young personality. Independence, individuality and freedom should be taught from the beginning, and the child should be encouraged as early as possible in life to think and act for himself. All parental control should be relinquished step by step as the ability for self-management is developed, and later on no restraint or false idea of duty to parenthood should hamper the dictates of the child's soul.

Parenthood is an office in life which passes from one to another, and is in essence a temporary giving of guidance and protection for a brief period, after which time it should then cease its efforts and leave the object of its attention free to advance alone. Be it remembered that the child for whom we may become a temporary guardian may be a much older and greater soul than ourselves, and spiritually our superior, so that control and protection should be confined to the needs of the young personality.

Parenthood is a sacred duty, temporary in its character and passing from generation to generation. It carries with it nothing but service and calls for no obligation in return from the young, since they must be left free to develop in their own way and become as fitted as possible to fulfil the same office in but a few years' time. Thus the child should have no restrictions, no obligations and no parental hindrances, knowing that parenthood had previously been bestowed on his father and mother and that it may be his duty to perform the same office for another.

Parents should be particularly on guard against any desire to mould the young personality according to their own ideas or wishes, and should refrain from any undue control or demand of favours in return for their natural duty and divine privilege of being the means of helping a soul to contact the world. Any desire for control, or wish to shape the young life for personal motives, is a terrible form of greed and should never be countenanced, for if in the young father or mother this takes root it will in later years lead them to be veritable vampires. If there is the least desire to dominate, it should be checked at the onset. We must refuse to be under the slavery of greed, which compels in us the wish to possess others. We must encourage in ourselves the art of giving, and develop this until it has washed out by its sacrifice every trace of adverse action.

The teacher should ever bear in mind that it is his office merely to be the agent of giving to the young guidance and an opportunity of learning the things of the world and of life, so that each child may absorb knowledge in his own way and, if allowed freedom, instinctively choose that which is necessary for the success of his life. Again, therefore, nothing more than the gentlest care and guidance should be given to enable the student to gain the knowledge he requires.

Children should remember that the office of parenthood, as emblematical of creative power, is divine in its mission, but that it calls for no restriction of development and no obligations which might hamper the life and work dictated to them by their own Soul. It is impossible to estimate in this present civilisation the untold suffering, the cramping of natures and the developing of dominant characters which the lack of a realisation of this fact produces. In almost every home parents and children build themselves prisons from entirely false motives and a wrong conception of the relationship of parent and child. These prisons bar the freedom, cramp the life, prevent the natural development and bring unhappiness to all concerned, and the mental, nervous and even physical disorders which afflict such people from a very large proportion indeed of the sickness of our present time.

It cannot be too firmly realised that every soul in incarnation is down here for the specific purpose of gaining experience and understanding, and of perfecting his personality towards those ideals laid down by the soul. No matter what our relationship be to each other, whether husband and wife, parent and child, brother and sister, or master and man, we sin against our Creator and against our fellow-men if we hinder from motives of personal desire the evolution of another soul. Our sole duty is to obey the dictates of our own conscience, and this will never for one moment brook the domination of another personality. Let everyone remember that his Soul has laid down for him a particular work, and that unless he does this work, though perhaps not consciously, he will inevitably raise a conflict between his Soul and personality which of necessity reacts in the form of physical disorders.

True, it may be the calling of any one individual to devote his life to one other alone, but before doing so let him be absolutely certain that this is the command of his Soul, and that it is not the suggestion of some other dominant personality over-persuading him, or false ideas of duty misdirecting him. Let him also remember that we come down into this world to win battles, to gain strength against those who would control us, and to advance to that stage when to pass through life doing our duty quietly and calmly, undeterred and uninfluenced by any living being, calmly guided always by the voice of our Higher Self. For very many their greatest battle will be in their own home, where before gaining their liberty to win victories in the world they will have to free themselves from the adverse domination and control of some very near relative.

Any individual, whether adult or child, part of whose work it is in this life to free himself from the dominant control of another, should remember the following: firstly, that his would-be oppressor should be regarded in the same way as we look upon an opponent in sport, as a personality with whom we are playing the game of Life, without the least trace of bitterness, and that if it were not for such opponents we should be lacking the opportunity of developing our own courage and individuality; secondly, that the real victories of life come through love and gentleness, and that in such a contest no force whatever must be used; that by steadily growing in his own nature, bearing sympathy, kindness and, if possible, affection – or, even better, love – towards the opponent, he may so develop that in time he may very gently and quietly follow the call of conscience without allowing the least interference.

Those who are dominant require much help and guidance to enable them to realise the great universal truth of Unity and to understand the joy of Brotherhood. To miss such things is to miss the real happiness of Life, and we must help such folk as far as lies within our power. Weakness on our part, which allows them to extend their influence, will in no way assist them; a gentle refusal to be under their control and an endeavour to bring to them the realisation of the joy of giving will help them along the upward path.

The gaining of our freedom, the winning of our individuality and independence, will in most cases call for much courage and faith. But in the darkest hours, and when success seems well-nigh impossible, let us ever remember that God's children should never be afraid, that our Souls only give us such tasks as we are capable of accomplishing, and that with our own courage and faith in the Divinity within us victory must come to all who continue to strive.

CHAPTER SIX

And now, dear brothers and sisters, when we realise that Love and Unity are the great foundations of our Creation, that we in ourselves are children of the Divine Love, and that the eternal conquest of all wrong and suffering will be accomplished by means of gentleness and love, when we realise all this, where in this beauteous picture are we to place such practices as vivisection and animal gland grafting? Are we still so primitive, so pagan, that we yet believe that by the sacrifice of animals we are enabled to escape the results of our own faults and failings? Nearly 2,500 years ago the Lord Buddha showed to the world the wrongness of sacrificing the lower creatures. Humanity already owes a mighty debt to the animals which it has tortured and destroyed, and far from any good resulting to man from such inhuman practices, nothing but harm and damage can be wrought to both the human and animal kingdoms. How far have we of the West wandered from those beautiful ideals of our mother India of old times, when so great was the love for the creatures of the earth that men were trained and skilled to attend the maladies and injuries of not only the animals, but also the birds. Moreover, there was vast sanctuaries for all types of life, and so averse were the people to hurting a lower creature that any man who any hunted was refused the attendance of a physician in time of sickness until he had vowed to relinquish such a practice.

Let us not speak against the men who practise vivisection, for numbers of these are working with truly humanitarian principles, hoping and striving to find some relief for human suffering; their motive is good enough, but their wisdom is poor, and they have little understanding of the reason of life. Motive alone, however right, is not enough; it must be combined with wisdom and knowledge.

Of the horror of the black magic associated with gland-grafting let us not even write, but implore every human being to shun it as ten thousand times worse than any plague, for it is a sin against God, man and animal.

With just such one or two exceptions there is no point in dwelling on the failure of modern medical science; destruction is useless unless we rebuild a better edifice, and as in medicine the foundation of the newer building is already laid, let us concentrate on adding one or two stones to that temple. Neither is adverse criticism of the profession today of value; it is the system which is mainly wrong, not the men; for it is a system whereby the physician, from economic reasons alone, has not the time for administering quiet, peaceful treatment or the opportunity for the necessary meditation and thought which should be the heritage of those who devote their lives to attendance on the sick. As Paracelsus said, the wise physician attends five, not fifteen patients in a day – an ideal impracticable in this age for the average practitioner.

The dawn of a new and better art of healing is upon us. A hundred years ago the Homœopathy of Hahnemann was as the first streak of the morning light after a long night of darkness, and it may play a big part in the medicine of the future. Moreover, the attention which is being given at the present time to improving conditions of life and providing purer and cleaner diet is an advance towards the prevention of sickness; and those movements which are directed to bring to the notice of the people both the connection between spiritual failings and disease and the healing which may be obtained through perfection of the mind, are pointing the way towards the coming of that bright sunshine in whose radiant light the darkness of disease will disappear.

Let us remember that disease is a common enemy, and that everyone of us who conquers a fragment of it is thereby helping not only himself but the whole of humanity. A certain, but definite, amount of energy will have to be expended before its overthrow is complete; let us one and all strive for this result, and those who are greater and stronger than the others may not only do their share, but materially assist their weaker brothers.

Obviously the first way to prevent the spread and increase of disease is for us to cease committing those actions which extend its power; the second, to wipe out from our natures our own defects, which would allow further invasion. The achievement of this is victory indeed; then, having freed ourselves, we are free to help others. And it is not so difficult as it may at first appear; we are but expected to do our best, and we know that this is possible for all of us if we will but listen to the dictates of our own Soul. Life does not demand of us unthinkable sacrifice; it asks us to travel its journey with joy in our heart and to be a blessing to those around, so that if we leave the world just that trifle better for our visit, then have we done our work.

The teachings of religions, if properly read, plead with us "to forsake all and follow Me," the interpretation of which is to give ourselves entirely up to the demands of our Higher Self, but not, as some imagine, to discard home and comfort, love and luxury; very far from this is the truth. A prince of the realm, with all the glories of the palace, may be a Godsend and a blessing indeed to his people, to his country – nay, even to the world; how much might have been lost had that prince imagined it his duty to enter a monastery. The offices of life in every branch, from the lowliest to the most exalted, have to be filled, and the Divine Guide of our destinies knows into which office to place us for our best advantage; all we are expected to do is to fulfil that duty cheerfully and well. There are saints at the factory bench and in the stokehold of a ship as well as among the dignitaries of religious orders. Not one of us upon this earth is being asked to do more than is within his power to perform, and if we strive to obtain the best within us, ever guided by our Higher Self, health and happiness is a possibility for each one.

For the greater part of the last two thousand years Western civilisation has passed through an age of intense materialism, and the realisation of the spiritual side of our natures and existence has been greatly lost in the attitude of mind which has placed worldly possessions, ambitions, desires and pleasures above the real things of life. The true reason of man's existence on earth has been overshadowed by his anxiety to obtain from his incarnation nothing but worldly gain. It has been a period when life has been very difficult because of the lack of the real comfort, encouragement and uplift which is brought by a realisation of greater things than those of the world. During the last centuries religions have to many people appeared rather as legends having no bearing on their lives instead of being the very essence of their existence. The true nature of our Higher Self, the knowledge of previous and later life, apart from this present one, has meant but very little to us instead of being the guide and stimulus of our every action. We have rather shunned the great things and attempted to make life as comfortable as possible by putting the superphysical out of our minds and depending upon earthly pleasures to compensate us for our trials. Thus have position, rank, wealth and worldly possessions become the goal of these centuries; and as all such things are transient and can only be obtained and held with much anxiety and concentration on material things, so has the real internal peace and happiness of the past generations been infinitely below that which is the due of mankind.

The real peace of the Soul and mind is with us when we are making spiritual advance, and it cannot be obtained by the accumulation of wealth alone, no matter how great. But the times are changing, and the indications are many that this civilisation has begun to pass from the age of pure materialism to a desire for the realities and truths of the universe. The general and rapidly increasing interest exhibited today for knowledge of superphysical truths, the growing number of those who are desiring information on existence before and after this life, the founding of methods to conquer disease by faith and spiritual means, the quest after the ancient teachings and wisdom of the East – all these are signs that people of the present time have glimpsed the reality of things. Thus, when we come to the problem of healing we can understand that this also will have to keep pace with the times and change its methods from those of gross materialism to those of a science founded upon the realities of Truth and governed by the same Divine laws which rule our very natures. Healing will pass from the domain of physical methods of treating the physical body to that of spiritual and mental healing, which by bringing about harmony between the Soul and mind will eradicate the very basic cause of disease, and then allow such physical means to be used as may be necessary to complete the cure of the body.

It seems quite possible that unless the medical profession realises these facts and advances with the spiritual growth of the people, the art of healing may pass into the hands of religious orders or into those of the trueborn healers of men who exist in every generation, but who yet have lived more or less unobserved, prevented from following their natural calling by the attitude of the orthodox. So that the physician of the future will have two great aims. The first will be to assist the patient to a knowledge of himself and to point out to him the fundamental mistakes he may be making, the deficiencies in his character which he should remedy, and the defects in his nature which must be eradicated and replaced by the corresponding virtues. Such a physician will have to be a great student of the laws governing humanity and of human nature itself, so that he may recognise in all who come to him those elements which are causing a conflict between the Soul and personality. He must be able to advise the sufferer how best to bring about the harmony required, what actions against Unity he must cease to perform and the necessary virtues he must develop to wipe out his defects. Each case will need a careful study, and it will only be those who have devoted much of their life to the knowledge of mankind and in whose heart burns the desire to help, who will be able to undertake successfully this glorious and divine work for humanity, to open the eyes of a sufferer and enlighten him on the reason of his being, and to inspire hope, comfort and faith which will enable him to conquer his malady.

The second duty of the physician will be to administer such remedies as will help the physical body to gain strength and assist the mind to become calm, widen its outlook and strive towards perfection, thus bringing peace and harmony to the whole personality. Such remedies there are in nature, placed there by the mercy of the Divine Creator for the healing and comfort of mankind. A few of these are known, and more are being sought at the present time by physicians in different parts of the world, especially in our Mother India, and there is no doubt that when such researches have become more developed we shall regain much of the knowledge which was known more than two thousand years ago, and the healer of the future will have at his disposal the wonderful and natural remedies, which were divinely placed for man to relieve his sickness.

Thus the abolition of disease will depend upon humanity realising the truth of the unalterable laws of our Universe and adapting itself with humility and obedience to those laws, thus bringing peace between its Soul and itself, and gaining the real joy and happiness of life. And the part of the physician will be to assist any sufferer to a knowledge of such truth and to point out to him the means by which he can gain harmony, to inspire him with faith in his Divinity which can overcome all, and to administer such physical remedies as will help in the harmonising of the personality and the healing of the body.

CHAPTER SEVEN

And now we come to the all-important problem, how can we help ourselves? How can we keep our mind and body in that state of harmony which will make it difficult or impossible for disease to attack us, for it is certain that the personality without conflict is immune from illness.

First let us consider the mind. We have already discussed at some length the necessity of seeking within ourselves those defects we possess which cause us to work against Unity and out of harmony with the dictates of the Soul, and of eliminating these faults by developing the opposing virtues. This can be done on the lines already indicated, and an honest self-examination will disclose to us the nature of our errors. Our spiritual advisers, true physicians and intimate friends should be able to assist us to obtain a faithful picture of ourselves, but the perfect method of learning this is by calm thought and meditation, and by bringing ourselves to such an atmosphere of peace that our Souls are able to speak to us through our conscience and intuition, and to guide us according to their wishes. If we can only set aside a short time every day, quite alone and in as quiet a place as possible, free from interruption, and merely sit or lie quietly, either keeping the mind a blank or calmly thinking of one's work in life, it will be found after a time that we get great help at such moments and, as it were, flashes of knowledge and guidance are given to us. We find that the questions of the difficult problems of life are unmistakably answered, and we become able to choose with confidence the right course. Throughout such times we should keep an earnest desire in the heart to serve humanity and work according to the dictates of our Soul.

Be it remembered that when the fault is found the remedy lies not in a battle against this and not in a use of will power and energy to suppress a wrong, but in a steady development of the opposite virtue, thus automatically washing from our natures all trace of the offender. This is the true and natural method of advancement and of the conquest of wrong, vastly easier and more effective than fighting a particular defect. To struggle against a fault increases its power, keeps out attention riveted on its presence, and brings us a battle indeed, and the most success we can then expect is conquest by suppression, which is far from satisfactory, as the enemy is still with us and may in a weak moment show itself afresh. To forget the failing and consciously to strive to develop the virtue which would make the former impossible, this is true victory.

For example, should there be cruelty in our nature, we can continually say, "I will not be cruel," and so prevent ourselves erring in that direction; but the success of this depends on the strength of the mind, and should it weaken we might for the moment forget our good resolve. But should we, on the other hand, develop real sympathy towards our fellow-men, this quality will once and for all make cruelty impossible, for we should shun the very act with horror because of our fellow-feeling. About this there is no suppression, no hidden enemy to come forward at moments when we are off our guard, because our sympathy will have completely eradicated from our nature the possibility of any act which could hurt another.

As we have previously seen, the nature of our physical maladies will materially help in pointing out to us the mental disharmony which is the basic cause of their origin; and another great factor of success is that we must have a zest for life and look upon existence not merely as a duty to be borne with as much patience as possible, developing a real joy in the adventure of our journey through this world.

Perhaps one of the greatest tragedies of materialism is the development of boredom and the loss of real inner happiness; it teaches people to seek contentment and compensation for troubles in earthly enjoyments and pleasures, and these can never bring anything but temporary oblivion of our difficulties. Once we begin to seek compensation for our trials at the hands of the paid jester we start a vicious circle. Amusement, entertainment and frivolity are good for us all, but not when we persistently depend upon these to alleviate our troubles. Worldly amusements of every kind have to be steadily increased in their intensity to keep their hold, and the thrill of yesterday becomes the bore of tomorrow. So we go on seeking other and greater excitements until we become satiated and can no longer obtain relief in that direction. In some form or another reliance on wordly entertainment makes Fausts of us all, and though perhaps we may not fully realise it in our conscious self, life becomes for us little more than a patient duty and all its true zest and joy, such as should be the heritage of every child and be maintained until our latest hours, departs from us. The extreme stage is reached today in the scientific efforts being evolved to obtain rejuvenation, prolongation of natural life and increase of sensual pleasures by means of devilish practices.

The state of boredom is responsible for the admittance into ourselves of much more disease than would be generally realised, and as it tends today to occur early in life, so the maladies associated with it tend to appear at a younger age. Such a condition cannot occur if we acknowledge the truth of our Divinity, our mission in the world, and thereby possess the joy of gaining experience and helping others. The antidote for boredom is to take an active and lively interest in all around us, to study life throughout the whole day, to learn and learn and learn from our fellow-men and from the occurrences in life the Truth that lies behind all things, to lose ourselves in the art of gaining knowledge and experience, and to watch for opportunities when we may use such to the advantage of a fellow-traveller. Thus every moment of our work and play will bring with it a zeal for learning, a desire to experience real things, real adventures and deeds worth while, and as we develop this faculty we shall find that we are regaining the power of obtaining joy from the smallest incidents, and occurrences we have previously regarded as commonplace and of dull monotony will become the opportunity for research and adventure. It is in the simple things of life – the simple things because they are nearer the great Truth – that real pleasure is to be found.

Resignation, which makes one become merely an unobservant passenger on the journey of life, opens the door to untold adverse influences which would never have an opportunity of gaining admittance as long as our daily existence brought with it the spirit and joy of adventure. Whatever may be our station, whether a worker in the city with its teeming myriads or a lonely shepherd on the hills, let us strive to turn monotony into interest, dull duty into a joyous opportunity for experience, and daily life into an intense study of humanity and the great fundamental laws of the Universe. In every place there is ample opportunity to observe the laws of Creation, either in the mountains or valleys or amongst our brother men. First let us turn life into an adventure of absorbing interest, when boredom will be no longer possible, and from the knowledge thus gained seek to harmonise our mind with our Soul and with the great Unity of God's Creation.

Another fundamental help to us is to put away all fear. Fear in reality holds no place in the natural human kingdom, since the Divinity within us, which is ourself, is unconquerable and immortal, and if we could but realise it we, as Children of God, have nothing of which to be afraid. In materialistic ages fear naturally increases in proportion to the amount of importance we place on earthly possessions (whether they be of the body itself or external riches), for if such things be our world, since they are so transient, so difficult to obtain and so impossible to hold save for a brief spell, they arouse in us the utmost anxiety lest we miss an opportunity of grasping them while we may, and we must of necessity live in a constant state of fear, conscious or sub-conscious, because in our inner self we know that such possessions may at any moment be snatched from us and that at the most we can only hold them for a brief life.

In this age the fear of disease has developed until it has become a great power for harm, because it opens the door to those things we dread and makes it easier for their admission. Such fear is really self-interest, for when we are earnestly absorbed in the welfare of others there is no time to be apprehensive of personal maladies. Fear at the present time is playing a great part in intensifying disease, and modern science has increased the reign of terror by spreading abroad to the general public its discoveries, which as yet are but half-truths. The knowledge of bacteria and the various germs associated with disease has played havoc in the minds of tens of thousands of people, and by the dread aroused in them has in itself rendered them more susceptible of attack. While lower forms of life, such as bacteria, may play a part in or be associated with physical disease, they constitute by no means the whole truth of the problem, as can be demonstrated scientifically or by everyday occurrences. There is a factor which science is unable to explain on physical grounds, and that is why some people become affected by disease while others escape, although both classes may be open to the same possibility of infection. Materialism forgets that there is a factor above the physical plane which in the ordinary course of life protects or renders susceptible any particular individual with regard to disease, of whatever nature it may be. Fear, by its depressing effect on our mentality, thus causing disharmony in our physical and magnetic bodies, paves the way for invasion, and if bacteria and such physical means were the sure and only cause of disease, then indeed there might be but little encouragement not to be afraid. But when we realise that in the worst epidemics only a proportion of those exposed to infection are attacked and that, as we have already seen, the real cause of disease lies in our own personality and is within our control, then have we reason to go about without dread and fearless, knowing that the remedy lies with ourselves. We can put all fear of physical means alone as a cause of disease out of our minds, knowing that such anxiety merely renders us susceptible, and that if we are endeavouring to bring harmony into our personality we need anticipate illness no more than we dread being struck by lightning or hit by a fragment of a falling meteor.

Now let us consider the physical body. It must never be forgotten that this is but the earthly habitation of the Soul, in which we dwell only for a short time in order that we may be able to contact the world for the purpose of gaining experience and knowledge. Without too much identifying ourselves with our bodies we should treat them with respect and care, so that they may be healthy and last the longer to do our work. Never for one moment should we become engrossed or over-anxious about them, but learn to be as little conscious of their existence as possible, using them as a vehicle of our Soul and mind and as servants to do our will. External and internal cleanliness are of great importance. For the former we of the West use our water too hot; this opens the skin and allows the admission of dirt. Moreover, the excessive use of soap renders the surface sticky. Cool or tepid water, either running as a shower bath or changed more than once is nearer the natural method and keeps the body healthier; only such an amount of soap as is necessary to remove obvious dirt should be used, and this should afterwards be well washed off in fresh water.

Internal cleanliness depends on diet, and we should choose everything that is clean and wholesome and as fresh as possible, chiefly natural fruit, vegetables and nuts. Animal flesh should certainly be avoided: first, because it gives rise to much physical poison in the body; secondly, because it stimulates an abnormal and excessive appetite; and thirdly, because it necessitates cruelty to the animal world. Plenty of fluid should be taken to cleanse the body, such as water and natural wines and products made direct from Nature's storehouse, avoiding the more artificial beverages of distillation.

Sleep should not be excessive, as many of us have more control over ourselves whilst awake than when asleep. The old saying, "Time to turn over, time to turn out," is an excellent guide as to when to rise.

Clothing should be as light in weight as is compatible with warmth; it should allow air to reach the body, and sunshine and fresh air should be permitted to contact the skin on all possible occasions. Water and sun bathing are great donors of health and vitality.

In all things cheerfulness should be encouraged, and we should refuse to be oppressed by doubt and depression, but remember that such are not of ourselves, for our Souls know only joy and happiness.

CHAPTER EIGHT

Thus we see that our conquest of disease will mainly depend on the following: firstly, the realisation of the Divinity within our nature and our consequent power to overcome all that is wrong; secondly, the knowledge that the basic cause of disease is due to disharmony between the personality and the Soul; thirdly, our willingness and ability to discover the fault which is causing such a conflict; and fourthly, the removal of any such fault by developing the opposing virtue.

The duty of the healing art will be to assist us to the necessary knowledge and means by which we may overcome our maladies, and in addition to this to administer such remedies as will strengthen our mental and physical bodies and give us greater opportunities of victory. Then shall we indeed be capable of attacking disease at its very base with real hope of success. The medical school of the future will not particularly interest itself in the ultimate results and products of disease, nor will it pay so much attention to actual physical lesions, or administer drugs and chemicals merely for the sake of palliating our symptoms, but knowing the true cause of sickness and aware that the obvious physical results are merely secondary it will concentrate its efforts upon bringing about the harmony between body, mind and soul which results in the relief and cure of disease. And in such cases as are undertaken early enough the correction of the mind will avert the imminent illness.

Amongst the types of remedies that will be used will be those obtained from the most beautiful plants and herbs to be found in the pharmacy of Nature, such as have been divinely enriched with healing powers for the mind and body of man.

For our own part we must practice peace, harmony, individuality and firmness of purpose and increasingly develop the knowledge that in essence we are of Divine origin, children of the Creator, and thus have within us, if we will but develop it, as in time we ultimately surely must, the power to attain perfection. And this reality must increase within us until it becomes the most outstanding feature of our existence. We must steadfastly practise peace, imagining our minds as a lake ever to be kept calm, without waves, or even ripples, to disturb its tranquillity, and gradually develop this state of peace until no event of life, no circumstance, no other personality is able under any condition to ruffle the surface of that lake or raise within us any feelings of irritability, depression or doubt. It will materially help to set apart a short time each day to think quietly of the beauty of peace and the benefits of calmness, and to realise that it is neither by worrying nor hurrying that we accomplish most, but by calm, quiet thought and action become more efficient in all we undertake. To harmonise our conduct in this life in accordance with the wishes of our own Soul, and to remain in such a state of peace that the trials and disturbances of the world leave us unruffled, is a great attainment indeed and brings to us that Peace which passeth understanding; and though at first it may seem to be beyond our dreams, it is in reality, with patience and perseverance, within the reach of us all.

We are not all asked to be saints or martyrs or men of renown; to most of us less conspicuous offices are allotted. But we are all expected to understand the joy and adventure of life and to fulfil with cheerfulness the particular piece of work which has been ordained for us by our Divinity.

For those who are sick, peace of mind and harmony with the Soul is the greatest aid to recovery. The medicine and nursing of the future will pay much more attention to the development of this within the patient than we do today when, unable to judge the progress of a case except by materialistic scientific means, we think more of the frequent taking of temperature and a number of attentions which interrupt, rather than promote, that quiet rest and relaxation of body and mind which are so essential to recovery. There is no doubt that at the very onset of, at any rate, minor ailments, if we could but get a few hours' complete relaxation and in harmony with our Higher Self the illness would be aborted. At such moments we need to bring down into ourselves but a fraction of that calm, as symbolised by the entry of Christ into the boat during the storm on the lake of Galilee, when He ordered, "Peace, be still."

Our outlook on life depends on the nearness of the personality to the Soul. The closer the union, the greater the harmony and peace, and the more clearly will shine the light of Truth and the radiant happiness which is of the higher realms; these will hold us steady and undismayed by the difficulties and terrors of the world, since they have their foundations on the Eternal Truth of God. The knowledge of Truth also gives to us the certainty that, however tragic some of the events of the world may appear to be, they form but a temporary stage in the evolution of man, and that even disease is in itself beneficent and works under the operation of certain laws designed to produce ultimate good and exerting a continual pressure towards perfection. Those who have this knowledge are unable to be touched or depressed or dismayed by those events which are such a burden to others, and all uncertainty, fear and despair go for ever. If we can but keep in constant communion with our own Soul, our Heavenly Father, then indeed is the world a place of joy, nor can any adverse influence be exerted upon us.

We are not permitted to see the magnitude of our own Divinity, or to realise the mightiness of our Destiny and the glorious future which lies before us; for, if we were, life would be no trial and would involve no effort, no test of merit. Our virtue lies in being oblivious for the most part to those great things, and yet having faith and courage to live well and master the difficulties of this earth. We can, however, by communion with our Higher Self keep that harmony which enables us to overcome all worldly opposition and make our journey along the straight path to fulfil our destiny, undeterred by the influences which would lead us astray.

Next must we develop individuality and free ourselves from all worldly influences, so that obeying only the dictates of our own Soul and unmoved by circumstances or other people we become our own masters, steering our bark over the rough seas of life without ever quitting the helm of rectitude, or at any time leaving the steering of our vessel to the hands of another. We must gain our freedom absolutely and completely, so that all we do, our every action – nay, even our every thought – derives its origin in ourselves, thus enabling us to live and give freely of our own accord, and of our own accord alone.

Our greatest difficulty in this direction may lie with those nearest to us in this age when the fear of convention and false standards of duty are so appallingly developed. But we must increase our courage, which with so many of us is sufficient to face the apparently big things of life but which yet fails at the more intimate trials. We must be able with impersonality to determine right and wrong and to act fearlessly in the presence of relative or friend. What a vast number of us are heroes in the outer world, but cowards at home! Though subtle indeed may be the means used to prevent us from fulfilling our Destiny, the pretence of love and affection, or a false sense of duty, methods to enslave us and keep us prisoners to the wishes and desires of others, yet must all such be ruthlessly put aside. The voice of our own Soul, and that voice alone, must be heeded as regards our duty if we are not to be hampered by those around us. Individuality must be developed to the utmost, and we must learn to walk though life relying on none but our own Soul for guidance and help, to take our freedom to gain every particle of knowledge and experience which may be possible.

At the same time we must be on our guard to allow to everyone their freedom also, to expect nothing from others but, on the contrary, to be ever ready to lend a helping hand to lift them upwards in times of their need and difficulty. Thus every personality we meet in life, whether mother, husband, child, stranger or friend, becomes a fellow-traveller, and any one of them may be greater or smaller than ourselves as regards spiritual development; but all of us are members of a common brotherhood and part of a great community making the same journey and with the same glorious end in view.

We must be steadfast in the determination to win, resolute in the will to gain the mountain summit; let us not give a moment's regret to the slips by the way. No great ascent was ever made without faults and falls, and they must be regarded as experiences which will help us to stumble less in the future. No thoughts of past errors must ever depress us; they are over and finished, and the knowledge thus gained will help to avoid a repetition of them. Steadily must we press forwards and onwards, never regretting and never looking back, for the past of even one hour ago is behind us, and the glorious future with its blazing light ever before us. All fear must be cast out; it should never exist in the human mind, and is only possible when we lose sight of our Divinity. It is foreign to us because as Sons of the Creator, Sparks of the Divine Life, we are invincible, indestructible and unconquerable. Disease is apparently cruel because it is the penalty of wrong thought and wrong action, which must result in cruelty to others. Hence the necessity of developing the love and brotherhood side of our natures to the utmost, since this will make cruelty in the future an impossibility.

The development of Love brings us to the realisation of Unity, of the truth that one and all of us are of the One Great Creation.

The cause of all our troubles is self and separateness, and this vanishes as soon as Love and the knowledge of the great Unity become part of our natures. The Universe is God rendered objective; at its birth it is God reborn; at its close it is God more highly evolved. So with man; his body is himself externalised, an objective manifestation of his internal nature; he is the expression of himself, the materialisation of the qualities of his consciousness.

In our Western civilisation we have the glorious example, the great standard of perfection and the teachings of The Christ to guide us. He acts for us as Mediator between our personality and our Soul. His mission on earth was to teach us how to obtain harmony and communion with our Higher Self, with Our Father which is in Heaven, and thereby to obtain perfection in accordance with the Will of the Great Creator of all.

Thus also taught the Lord Buddha and other great Masters, who have come down from time to time upon earth to point out to men the way to attain perfection. There is no halfway path for humanity. The Truth must be acknowledged, and man must unite himself with the infinite scheme of Love of his Creator.

And so come out, my brothers and sisters, into the glorious sunshine of the knowledge of your Divinity, and earnestly and steadfastly set to work to join in the Grand Design of being happy and communicating happiness, uniting with that great band of the White Brotherhood whose whole existence is to obey the wish of their God, and whose great joy is in the service of their younger brother men.

– XIII –

Some Fundamental Considerations
of Disease & Cure

[Homœopathic World, 1930]

To understand disease, its object, its nature, and its cure, we must in part comprehend the reason of our being and the laws of our Creator in relation to us.

It is essential to realise that man has two aspects, a spiritual and a physical; and that of these two, the physical is infinitely the less important.

Under the guidance of our Spiritual Self, our Immortal Life, Man is born to gain knowledge and experience; and to perfect himself as a physical being.

The physical body alone, without communion with the Spiritual, is as an empty shell, a cork upon the waters, but when there is union, life is a joy, an adventure of absorbing interest; a journey yielding happiness, health and knowledge.

Our evolution began as a new born babe, without knowledge, and with the whole interest self-centred. Desires being limited to comfort, food and warmth. Then as we advance comes the desire for power, and so for a time we continue to be self-centred, desiring only our own gain and worldly ambitions.

Then comes the turning point: the birth of the wish to be of service to others, and then begins the battle, for in the course of our further evolution we have to turn self into selfless, separation into unity, to gain all the knowledge and experience which the world can teach us; and to transmute all the human qualities into their opposing virtues.

However we learn slowly, one lesson at a time, but we must if we are to be well and happy, learn the particular lesson given to us by our spiritual self.

We are not all learning the same lesson at the same time. One is conquering pride, another fear, another hate, and so on, but the essential factor for health is that we do learn the lesson set for us.

It matters not our stage of advancement, whether aborigine or disciple, is of no consequence as regards health; but what is important is that we, whatever our station, live in harmony with the dictates of our soul. Whether it be to gain rank and wealth, or to live the sacrificing life of a martyr, health depends on obeying the commands, and being in accord with our own Spiritual Self.

Our soul places us in that station of life and gives to us that calling, be it bootblack or monarch, prince or pauper, which is best suited for our evolution, and where we can most readily learn the lesson needed, and whatever our position, it is only necessary to do the particular work laid down for us, and all will be well.

Disease is the result of a conflict, when the personality refuses to obey the dictates of the soul, when there is disharmony, disease, between the Higher or Spiritual Self, and the lower personality as we know ourselves.

None of us is given more than we can accomplish, nor are we asked to do more than is within our power.

Life then resolves itself into the effort of transmuting the lower qualities of self into the higher virtues of selfless unity. Not by drastic nor frenzied efforts, but by a slow, gradual and should be happy evolution.

During our sojourn in search of perfection, there are various stages. To transmute self into selfless, desire into desireless, separateness into unity is not done in a moment but by gradual steady evolution, and we have to master stage by stage as we progress. Some stages may be comparatively easy, some exceedingly difficult, and then it is that disease occurs, because it is at those times that we fail to follow our Spiritual Self, that the conflict arises which produces illness.

According to the particular stage at which we are failing, so on the physical place does a definite mentality develop, with its consequent results both on the patient and those associated with him. It is this mentality which teaches the physician the real fundamental cause of the patient's trouble, and gives to him the keynote of successful treatment.

From this can be ascertained the effort the patient is expected to make, where he is failing, and thus can be deduced the correct treatment for his welfare.

Hahnemann taught that "Like cures like." This is true up to a point, but the word 'cures' is a little misleading. Like repels like might be more accurate.

Disease itself is like curing like, or better, like repelling like.

The reason of disease is to cause us to cease wrong actions; the most effective method to harmonise our personality with our soul. Were it not for pain how could we really know that cruelty hurt? Had we never any loss, could we realise the suffering caused by robbery? True we should learn our lessons on the mental plane, and so save physical suffering, but many of us fail to do this. And so disease is sent to us to hasten our evolution. Cruel as it may seem in our narrow outlook, it is in reality beneficent in its nature. It is the method adopted by our own Fatherly Loving Soul, to bring us to the path of understanding.

Moreover, let it be remembered that suffering (although we certainly should by wisdom avoid it) is in a way a privilege; since it indicates that the personality has reached that stage of development when correcting is possible; very small babies are not chastised.

Hence immediately can be seen how disease can be avoided; could we but listen to the voice of our Spiritual Self, but keep in harmony with our soul, no such severe lesson would be needed, and we could live disease free.

Thus it is the work of the physician to assist his patient to that end, by spiritual, mental, and physical assistance.

The genius of Hahnemann realising the nature and reason of disease, used like remedies, which, by temporarily intensifying the illness, hastened its end. He used like poisons to repel the poisons from the body.

But having contemplated where his genius left us, let us advance a step further forward, and we shall see that there is even a new and better way.

If a patient has a mental error, a conflict between spiritual and physical self will result, and disease will be the product. The error may be repelled, the poison driven from the body, but a vacuum is left, an adverse force has gone, but a space exists where it has been situated.

The perfect method is not so much to repel the adverse influence, as to draw in its opposing virtue; and by means of this virtue flood out the fault. This is the law of opposites, of positive and negative.

For example: a patient is suffering pain because there is cruelty in his nature. He may suppress that quality by constantly determining, "I will not be cruel," but this means a long and strenuous battle, and should he succeed in eliminating cruelty, there is a gap, a void. But should that patient concentrate on the positive side, to develop sympathy, and flood his nature with that virtue, cruelty without any further effort is replaced and for all time becomes impossible.

So the perfect science of healing teaches and assists the patient to develop that virtue which will make, once and for all, immunity against that adverse quality, which it is his particular battle to efface.

This is not the healing of "Thou shalt not," but of "Blessed are they."

Another great principle of Hahnemann's genius may be considered here: the teaching of curing from within out.

The mind must be healed first, and the body will follow. To cure the body and not the mind might be very serious for the patient, as the body gains at the expense of the soul, and at the best it is only a lesson deferred. It were better to lose a body than that the lesson were missed.

Therefore the work of the physician is two-fold, to assist his patient to correct his spiritual failing, and to give him such remedies as will help him to effect this on the physical plane; so that the healthier mind will effect a cure of the body.

For the latter it is essential that the remedies chosen should be life-giving and uplifting; of such vibrations that elevate.

In the choice of these we must consider their evolutionary status as regard to man.

Metals are sub-human. The use of animals would necessitate cruelty, and no trace of such must occur in the divine art of healing. Thus we are left with the vegetable kingdom. Plants are of three types. The first group is relatively below that of man in their evolution; of such are the primitive varieties, the seaweeds, the cactus, the dodder, etc. Also those which have been used for wrong purposes, some of which are poisonous: Henbane, Belladonna, and the orchids are examples.

A second class, on the same relative scale as man, which are harmless, and may be used as food.

But there is a third group, relatively as high or higher than average mankind. Of these we must choose our remedies, for they have been given the power to heal and to bless.

Moreover there is no cruelty entailed in this: for as these plants desire to be used for the benefit of human nature, a blessing is conferred upon them during their service to man.

The first group, by lowering the vibrations of the body, renders it unfit for habitation by the Spiritual Self, and hence may cause death. But the last class have the power to elevate our vibrations, and thus draw down spiritual power, which cleanses mind and body, and heals.

Our work as physicians is thus outlined: To study human nature, so that we may be enabled to assist our patients to a knowledge of themselves, and advise them how to harmonise their personalities with their souls, and also to administer such beneficent remedies that will raise the vibrations of the personality, and make it a more acceptable habitation for the soul; and thus develop the virtue required to bring that harmony between the Higher and lower self, which results in perfect health.

And now let us consider the practical aspect as regards diagnosis and treatment.

There are primarily seven main divisions into which we have to place our patients.

An individual may err, according to the particular lesson being learnt, on any of the following fundamental principles:

1. Power
2. Intellectual knowledge
3. Love
4. Balance
5. Service
6. Wisdom
7. Spiritual Perfection

Before proceeding further let it again be emphasised that the presence of disease indicates that the personality is in conflict with the soul.

Qualities and virtues are relative, and what is a virtue in one, may be a fault in another. To seek power alone may be right in a young soul, and cause no conflict between the personality and the Spiritual Self, but what is right here would be out of place and hence wrong in the more advanced stage of discipleship, when the Soul has decided for the personality to give instead of to take.

Hence a quality of itself cannot be judged right or wrong, without considering the evolutionary status of the individual.

What we know as evil is good out of place.

But the presence of disease indicates that there are qualities in the personality, which the Soul is endeavouring to remove, because such qualities are below the evolutionary standard of that individual.

Moreover the patient must be persistently refusing to listen to the voice of Conscience, refusing to gain his experience on the mental place, and hence the necessity for the more severe lesson which is taught by illness.

From the mentality of our patients can we discern the error which they are making the particular failure of the personality to keep pace with the evolutionary standard desired by the Soul.

Errors on each of the seven principles will give types as follows:

1.	POWER	Tyrant	Autocrat	Sensationalist
2.	INTELLECT	Magician	Destroyer	Satyr
3.	LOVE	Inquisitor	Hate	Rage
4.	BALANCE	Ecstatic	Weather Vane	Hysteric
5.	SERVICE	Self-righteous	Egoist	Flirt
6.	WISDOM	Agnostic	Fool	Clown
7.	SPIRITUAL PERFECTION	Enthusiast	Puritan	Monk

It matters not what may be the physical disease of our patient, we have to comprehend to which of the above types he belongs.

Nor must we expect the characteristics always to be strongly marked, for in many cases there may be only a trace of the adverse type remaining in their natures, but still it is essential to understand exactly their fundamental error, however slight this may be, to ensure successful treatment.

Moreover in many patients who come to us, their personalities are almost crushed out by some dominant relative or friend, and in some of these it may be easier to obtain a diagnosis from the dominator, for they will be of the same type as the patient; because again it is a case of like repelling like, for we are placed amongst those who have our own failings, more strongly marked, so that we may realise the suffering such adverse actions cause.

Before considering the above types in more detail, and so far as the research has proceeded giving the remedies associated with each, let us discuss the methods of dosage.

Here again the law of Hahnemann holds, not to repeat whilst improvement is taking place.

The remedies to be described are beneficent in action, and cause no aggravation nor reaction for their effect is to uplift.

They are prepared in the third, fourth and seventh potencies.

To begin a case a dose of the third maybe given twice or three times a day until improvement is well marked, then cease. So long as progress is being made give no further treatment, but if there is a relapse, administer three or four more doses, and so on, each time after, less should be required. Only resort to the fourth or seventh, should the lower potency fail to hold.

If you had a friend who had suffered a great loss and was in despair, you would at first visit him often to cheer and comfort him; but as he became reconciled the visits might safely grow less.

So use these potencies; they are friends and blessings to the distressed, but as Hahnemann foresaw, even the sick must fight their battles and not come to depend upon even beneficent medicines; and so when better, it is necessary to fight along alone, as far as possible, without again calling for help until really necessary.

And of course the more a patient strives to correct the fault which lies behind his illness, the longer will the potency hold.

And now we come to a description of some of the types associated with disease, and the remedies given to cure these.

Here I must offer my gratitude to Dr F.J. Wheeler of Southport, for his very great assistance with regard to the clinical results he has obtained with these remedies, his whole-hearted collaboration over a considerable period, and his financial generosity on a large scale, which alone has made possible the discovery of many of these remedies.

(All remedies to be mentioned in these articles are stocked by Messrs Nelsons and Co, 73, Duke Street, Grosvenor Square, London, W1. Messrs Epps, Thatcher and Co., 60, Jermyn Street, London, SW1).

THE REMEDIES AND THEIR TYPES

The full botanical name of each remedy is as follows:

1.	AGRIMONIA	*Agrimonia epatoria*
2.	CERATO	*Ceratostigma willmottiana*
3.	CICHORIUM	*Cichorium intybus*
4.	CLEMATIS FLORA	*Clematis erecta flora*
5.	COTYLEDON	*Cotyledon umbilicus*
6.	CENTAURIUM..................	*Erythraea centaurium*

7.	IMPATIENS	*Impatiens roylei*
8.	MIMULUS........................	*Mimulus luteus*
9.	SCLERANTHUS	*Scleranthus annuus*
10.	ARVENSIS	*Sonchus arvensis*
11.	VERBENA.........................	*Verbena officinalis*

AGRIMONIA

THE INQUISITOR

This type is not always easy to diagnose as they mask their troubles.

They are often, to casual appearance, genial and full of life's interest, and decidedly likeable people. They often drink heavily, though not to obvious excess: may be addicts to drugs: and desire excitements and a full busy life. Thus they hide the suffering within.

One feels with them that there is a tragedy beneath though they rarely admit it even to their best friends. Inside, they suffer torments: great fear of the present and especially the future, which may drive them to suicide. They care nothing for danger, and are reckless in all ways. They have no peace: are active: restless: always doing: require little sleep: retire late.

They are usually very much interested in occultism and magic. They are in reality tormented souls who are weary of their sufferings, and would prefer death as a better alternative, though outwardly, they put up a brave fight with forced cheerfulness.

Frequently it is found that they are worried by some tormenting individual, though their persecutor may be on another plane.

The remedy brings peace: removes their torments: decreases the desire for stimulants: and gives them calm.

CERATO

THE FOOL

For those seeking to go forward, yet bewildered, unable to define right and wrong. Lack of knowledge makes them indiscreet in their choice of friends; in their work; their pleasure; and the influences they allow to come into their lives. Those whose intentions are good, but whose discretion is poor.

They concentrate too much on the details of life, and miss the main principles: convention and small things count above main issues.

They frequently miss their opportunities because of minor influences; and throw away their life's work on account of the adverse persuasion of some relative or companion. They greatly exaggerate the duties they hold to another fellow-mortal; binding themselves to some dominant personality when they should be serving the many.

They are weak and make excuses for their persecutor, as a woman will defend the drunken husband who beats her. They are inwardly unhappy, because, subconsciously, they realise that they are wasting their time: they are quietly discontented with their own efforts. Could they but be persuaded really to grasp the truth of their foolishness, they would improve. This class is the victim of the Egoist and the Destroyer.

This remedy brings wisdom to comprehend the truth: judgement to define right and wrong: and encourages strength and ability to keep the right path when realised.

CICHORIUM

THE EGOIST

These people desire to use others for their own purposes; they are possessive, the opposite of the loving self-sacrificing mother. They are loquacious; with rapid continuous talking, and weary others with their chatter. They are poor listeners, always bringing the conversation back to their own interests. They fuss and worry others over trivial things: they seem to desire to give others no peace, no rest. They are self-centred, hard natured, and full of their own affairs. Their very vivacity, at first perhaps entertaining and attractive, soon wearies those around.

They desire company and hate to be alone, in fact fear solitude, since they depend upon others for their supply of vitality. They obtain sympathy and attention through tales of self-pity, and through their maladies: they make much of their troubles, and will simulate illness if they find it brings to them care from others.

When unable to have their own way on important things, they are spiteful, revengeful, vindictive, and cruel. They are very persistent and scheming to obtain their own ends.

As relations or friends, they are demanding, and, although it is not always realised, they are a great drain of vitality.

They are often thin and pale; greasy skin: feel the cold. Chronic headache: indigestion: constipation: catarrh: colds: irritability, are common ailments. Worry upsets them much, often causing abdominal discomfort or pain. Appetite large.

The remedy, in addition to relieving any symptoms of this class of patient, stimulates sympathy with others, which is their lesson: hence turns their attention more from themselves, and so, out of sympathy for their victims, they cease their aggression: and may become of service to those they previously devitalised.

The lesson is through devotion to others, to become selfless.

CLEMATIS FLORA

THE ECSTATIC

For those who make "dreams their master": live in their ideals; but do little on the practical side. Often book-lovers, and become lost in their reading, especially in earlier life.

They are carried away with religious or patriotic movements, becoming temporarily absorbed, and neglecting their ordinary duties. They will turn their attention from one enterprise to another rapidly.

They tend to form too strong attachments to other personalities, and place themselves under their power; this is voluntary and without fear and may be associated with deep affection and the desire never to be parted. The stronger personality may use his influence adversely during life; or, after death, call his partner over: hence the absence of fighting disease.

They have no great hold on life: it is not very much to them: they show little resistance to disease: seem to have no fear of death, nor desire to get well. They are placid: calm: resigned in illness, not from patient courage, but because of their indifference.

Thus they have two phases: ecstacy concerning ideals and, in illness, calm resignation.

The remedy brings stability: and places the patient on a more practical plane; brings them 'down to earth'; and so enables them to fulfil their work in this world.

COTYLEDON

THE HYSTERIC

These patients have emotional instability. They are excitable: nervous: useless in emergency: they become flustered over trifles.

They are unreliable because of their uncertainty and lack of control. They wish to do well, but fail utterly owing to their irresponsible nature. Their weakness causes them much anxiety, especially their inability to conquer their faults.

Many cases of hysteria: hystero-epilepsy: and hysterical paralyses come into this group.

The remedy stimulates the ability of steadfastness, calm courage, and quiet determination to win.

It gives the characteristics of the Roman centurion 'faithful unto death'; just as *Scleranthus* develops those of the commander.

CENTAURIUM

THE AUTOCRAT

These people, in their striving for power, have lost their sense of proportion of their own relative position and importance in the world.

They are noisy in speech and movement: demanding of attention: impatient: and particular over the details of their own wants and comfort. They are overbearing and full of their own achievements.

Usually big physique: high colour: they tend to suffer from high blood pressure, and its companion ills.

The remedy tends to bring softness and gentleness into these natures: and to reduce the tension both mental and physical.

IMPATIENS

THE ENTHUSIAST

This remedy is for acute pain, no matter what the cause: it is the severity of the pain which is its indication. In some cases it has given relief after morphia had failed.

It is also for acute mental suffering: again the intensity being the guide.

It is useful in those people who (no matter their apparent status) are making a great effort to overcome some adverse quality: hence the intensity of the suffering when they fear failure.

In addition the remedy brings peace, and a definite mental uplift, of which the patients are usually very conscious.

MIMULUS

HATE

This type suffers from exhaustion, weariness, being easily tired. They have vague fears: dread of things unknown, which makes them nervous: sleep is poor and unrefreshing.

They are very averse to, and exhausted by, noise, talking, and especially to being questioned. They desire to be alone and quiet.

They are often interested in spiritualism, and are of the medium type.

Their exhaustion and prostration is out of all proportion to physical cause.

This condition is often seen after Influenza.

The remedy brings calmness and loss of fear. It develops pity in the nature which is the lesson required.

SCLERANTHUS

THE WEATHER VANE

The key-note to this type is lack of stability and confidence. There is no self-reliance, hence they are always seeking the advice of others; and are swayed to and fro between the various opinions of their friends. They are unable to make decisions, and suffer mental torture as a result.

They are nervous: restless: shirk responsibility: and avoid people except when they seek help. Their fault is that they rely entirely on the intellect and not at all on their intuition. They have difficulty of concentration of mind, as this swings from one subject to another.

They are examples of extremes: first depression, then joy, at one moment optimistic, another pessimistic: they are unreliable and uncertain, because of their constantly changing outlook: one day a good companion, another moody: sometimes charitable and extravagant, sometimes mean and miserly.

Their symptoms, temperatures, etc, all come and go, rise and fall with rapid fluctuations, following the example of the mental state.

The remedy brings clearness of mental vision: ability for quick decision: determination and calmness in face of difficulties. It develops the characteristics of the efficient commander, as *Cotyledon* brings out the qualities of a good soldier.

ARVENSIS

THE DESTROYER

These people are in the depths of gloom; no light; no joy; no happiness. They are intensely unhappy as may be seen in their faces; and they brood darkness over others.

Their complexion is muddy, of a yellowish or orange brown.

They look always on the dark side of things and are despondent; and refuse to enjoy what opportunities they have of pleasure: always brooding on the dark side of life: they wallow in all that is morbid, and infect and depress others with their gloom.

The remedy brings sunshine into their lives, and helps them to cheer others.

VERBENA

THE PURITAN

For those of high ideals, striving to live an exalted life yet failing on some point.

The patient may be too stern, too rigid in principle, too narrow-minded in outlook, endeavouring to mould the world too much to his own ideals. Of highest principle, yet intolerant of faults in others; too severe on himself; excessive self-denial driving the joy out of life. Failing in generosity, charity, or chivalry.

They may waver from their standards in times of difficulties.

This remedy softens the nature, broadens the outlook, increases the generosity and patience, and encourages steadfastness in face of trial.

The lesson of this class is: – tolerance: patience: broadmindedness.

The above are certain types. There are other remedies necessary to complete the series, which it is hoped will be found and published in due course.

In medicine we must study the great principles of life if we are to be of help to our fellow-men.

In this world we are all on the same path, fellow-travellers on the road to perfection. We have ultimately to gain all the knowledge and experience which can be learned on earth: to change completely self into selfless, and to develop all the virtues to the utmost purity.

The particular lesson of the present is the keynote to our type. We are not placed in the luxury of a palace to overcome hardship bravely: nor do we come as paupers to learn the wise control of wealth. The circumstances, the environment, and the people amongst whom he is placed, all should be indications to the wise physician of the battle which the patient has to undertake. Our very faults and failings are the reverse of the virtue to which we aspire. To conquer craving we may be born into a family where drunkenness is common: to conquer hate, we may have to be born amongst those who are cruel. In fact, often the adverse qualities which we have received by heredity are the ones which we have particularly come to eliminate. And if we fail to learn our lesson on the mental place, we must suffer the result of our failure from others until the fault is completely eradicated in ourselves.

Thus our failings, and adverse companions, and circumstances are the opposite of the virtues we are attempting to attain.

In treatment it is essential to diagnose the type of the individual, and the virtue he is endeavouring to perfect; and, until such time as we are capable of administering Spiritual healing, we must prescribe that remedy which has the power to assist the patient in his struggle.

Thus we only judge the faults and failings and the adverse circumstances of a patient as indications of the good he is endeavouring to develop. In opposition to this, we must earnestly seek for the positive good: find out any virtue, especially a predominating virtue, which our patient has when at his best, and give him the remedy which will so increase that virtue that it will flood out of his nature his faults.

Our work as physicians is to seek for the best, either by direct means or by studying the faults which have to be overcome; and to develop and bring out that best to the utmost of our power. It should be our endeavour, by means of the agencies at our disposal, to keep our patients at their highest standard, and thus enable them to march forward.

And now, Brother Physicians, there is a simple and more perfect method of potentisation of remedies than we have hitherto used.

Let not the simplicity of this method deter you from its use, for you will find the further your researches advance, the greater you will realise the simplicity of all Creation.

The remedies* described in this article were prepared as follows. A glass vessel, as thin as possible, was nearly filled with clean water, preferably from a spring. Into this were placed sufficient of the blooms of the plant to cover the surface completely. A cloudless day was chosen, and the blooms picked after they had had about two hours' sunshine upon them. The vessel was then placed in the sun and its position changed from time to time so that the sunlight passed directly down the orifice as well as bathing the whole.

About a quarter of the fluid was drawn off at the third, fourth, and seventh hours, and about 20 per cent of pure alcohol added to each. This may be used direct as a third, fourth, and seventh potency.

Let it be noticed in this that the four elements are involved: the earth to nurture the plant: the air from which it feeds: the sun or fire to enable it to impart its power: and water to collect and to be enriched with its beneficent magnetic healing.

There are two kinds of errors: the errors of omission and the errors of commission.

If we have in our natures a virtue which we are failing to develop, this is a failing of omission; it is like to the man who hid his talent; and this fault is connected with latent disease. A disease which like a cloud hangs over us, yet never need descend upon us can we but in time realise our mistake, and then develop the virtue required of us.

Active wrong is connected with active disease:when we, against the choice of our conscience, are doing those things which we know are contrary to the Laws of the Unity and Brotherhood of Man.

Thus it is for the true physician to be enabled to assist his patients by pointing out to them, either the latent virtue which they are failing to develop, or the adverse quality which they are exercising against the dictates of their better Self. And it is for us also to administer those remedies, so beneficent in their nature that they have the power to enable man to harmonise his conduct in this life so as to render it acceptable to that Divine Being from Whom all goodness springs.

Finally, let us remember in all our work that disease is for man to conquer, and that if we will but strive, it has been given to humanity, under Divine Guidance, to overcome everything that is adverse: for

*With the exception of *Impatiens, Mimulus,* and *Cotyledon,* which were prepared earlier by trituration.

the Love and Truth of our Creator is Omnipotent, and Good must ultimately have complete victory.

Could we but realise this Truth in all its sufficiency, the conquest over disease could be with us even now.

— XIV —

Some New Remedies & New Uses

[*Homœopathic World*, February 1930]

Impatiens Roylei – Mimulus Luteus – Clematis Vitalba –
Cupressus – Cotyledon umbilicus.

To those of us who have studied the science of Homœopathy there is
left no doubt as to its wonderful power in the cause of healing or the
magnificent results that can consistently be expected by the skilled
prescriber. Moreover, we must all admire the purity of its teaching
and its constant aim to use only the remedies to be found in Nature's
Materia Medica. And it seems that the possession of this precious
treasure should stimulate us to further exertions, for undoubtedly
with patience and perseverance a remedy can be found for every
disease, in those patients wishing to be cured, and it may even be also
possible to find those which will overcome that desire for ill-health, so
difficult in our present state of knowledge to combat.

We have much to discover, but we must not be afraid of the task. A
vast time may be required, but we must all attempt to do our share in
the building of that glorious temple of healing which will ultimately
be the agent to drive disease from the face of the earth.

There is much to learn of the gathering and preparation of herbs;
many points require consideration if the maximum, instead of the
medium result is to be obtained: the natural habitat, age, condition
and particular part of the plant; the planetary influences; the time of
day, and, by no means the least important, the mental attitude of the
physician, which should be one of whole-hearted devotion to the work
in hand in the cause of humanity. At present our knowledge on some
of these points is sadly small, but we must do the best in our power,
and as we proceed, greater experience will make the task simpler.

The following notes of remedies are being humbly offered to you,
as I feel they cover some of the points which are amongst the more

difficult to treat in the ordinary way, and it is hoped that they may be found of as much value to the profession in general as to those few who have already proved their value in practice. These remedies were prepared with all precautions, instruments and glass-ware being heated at 160° C. for four hours, corks at 160° C. for twenty minutes, and a clean overall worn for each individual trituration. The first potency was made immediately on the site of collection. Each potency was triturated with *sacch. lac.* by hand for twenty-one minutes in a glass mortar with a glass pestle. This was done up to the seventh centesimal, after which succussion was adopted.

IMPATIENS ROYLEI

A native of Kashmir, rarely found growing wild in the British Isles. Mauve flowers only used.

Three different series have been prepared: two on separate dates in September, 1928, and one in September, 1929. Although all have been effective, the most active is the last obtained, which is the one now stocked by Messrs Nelson and Co.

It is indicated in acute pain of nerve type, and it not only often gives rapid relief, but in many cases apparently effects a cure of the nerve condition. It has also a beneficent action, and patients frequently report, in addition to relief of symptoms, a much improved mental state with loss of depression and fears, a generally brighter outlook being obtained.

Amongst cases successfully treated may be mentioned intense headaches, sciaticas, acute neuralgias, tic douloureux, and acute pain in malignant disease.

The indication for its use is excruciating and very acute pain, no matter what the cause; in some cases it has given relief after morphia has failed.

MIMULUS LUTEUS

A native of North America, found occasionally in the British Isles. Flower only used.

It is the mentals of this remedy which are the most important; its physical side is usually the result of mental strain. They comprise depression, vague unknown fears, marked desire for quietness, aversion to talking and to being questioned, loss of ability to fight for personal individuality (the patient will do anything to avoid controversy). In more marked cases there is often in addition great weakness, tiredness, tachycardia, no desire for food, and frequently a 5 pm aggravation.

Amongst some of the most brilliant results treated with this remedy have been cases of post-influenzal debility, and others of patients who have broken down under the strain of domestic unhappiness due to overpowering relations or even friends.

This remedy helps in a remarkable manner patients who are devitalised by other too powerful personalities, and returns to them their confidence and ability to stand up and face the difficulties of daily life, causing at the same time a marked improvement in their general physical health.

CLEMATIS VITALBA

A native of the British Isles.

Three separate preparations have been made of this – prima, secunda and tertia, to be used according to the severity of the case, prima for the mildest.

This is another remedy in which the mentals are the important character. The patients have little desire for life, from the state of finding no enjoyment to that of desire for death. Unlike those of the *Mimulus* type, they have no fears, but are calm and of the daydreaming type, content to be left alone and with no wish to do anything more than is absolutely necessary. They often require many hours of sleep at night and are difficult to wake. The whole constitution is sluggish and the complexion often pale and muddy; they easily contract disease, but are not in the least perturbed. They are not nearly so sensitive to noise as the patients of the *Mimulus* class.

The mentality is like that of an individual who has lost all that is dear to him and has little ambition to survive, whose life becomes a patient duty, merely to be borne until release occurs. Hence the absence of fear of or aversion to illness; indeed, many wish for this in the hope of passing out, and make no fight for recovery.

The physician with keen observation will notice this condition in all grades of severity in his practice, from the mild day-dreamer to the subject of the most hopeless, yet patient and placid, depression. The

severest type is sleepy sickness, in which this remedy as proved
effective and there is every reason to hope that it will also be useful in
some types of coma.

CUPRESSUS

The red vessels from the tip of the leaves only used.

This is proving a most valuable remedy in chronic catarrh and its
sequelæ, especially if the infection is of the staphylococcic or streptococcic type, and it is especially indicated in: Catarrh of the post-
nasal passages, the Eustachian tube and middle ear, and the frontal
sinuses. Headache associated with catarrh. Chronic colds, in connection with which there is evidence to show that it is prophylactic, and,
if given early, in some cases frequently aborts an attack.

Among the more striking results have been cures of chronic deaf-
ness following middle ear disease of over twenty years' duration, and
of frontal headaches, which in one case had been continuous for over
three years.

Adult Cupressus cases are often of florid, congested complexion.

COTYLEDON UMBILICUS (*Prima*)

A native of the British Isles, found mostly in the south and south-
west.

This remedy has proved effective in epilepsy of the petit mal type,
when other treatment has failed. It also appears to be helpful in
eliminating the after-effects of long-continued doses of bromide by
clearing the mentality and restoring the natural brightness of the
patient.

These remedies can all be obtained from the third to the twenty-
eighth centesimal. The number of cases which have been treated with
these remedies is considerable, yet so far it has not been necessary to
use above the seventh centesimal. *Cupressus* must certainly not be
started above the third, or it tends to give marked aggravation.
Should this occur, it responds rapidly to strong doses of peppermint.

If physicians using any of these remedies find that important
symptoms, not here mentioned, are relieved, it would greatly help the
work of completing the provings, if they would kindly report them.

– XV –

An Effective Method of Preparing Vaccines for Oral Administration

[*Medical World*, January 1930]

During the last ten years a new method of preparing vaccines for oral administration has been thoroughly explored, extensively used and beyond all doubt proved to be of great therapeutic value in cases of chronic disease. A large number of practitioners in the British Isles, America, Germany, France and other countries can testify to the value of this method to such an extent as to leave no doubt that an important therapeutic agent has been added to the materia medica of our science.

There are such definite advantages in the oral method of administration of vaccines that any advancement in this direction must naturally be welcomed by practitioners and public alike. Firstly, one of the great drawbacks of hypodermic injections is the necessity of adding antiseptic, a substance which all of us would wish to avoid introducing into the tissues. Secondly, very many patients have a distinct antagonism to vaccines in the usual form and are thus debarred from the benefits of this form of therapy; they have, however frequently no objection whatever, when the preparation is given orally.Thirdly, the pain and swelling of local reaction is entirely avoided, and in most cases general reaction is markedly less, a matter of considerable importance to those of low vitality and to the aged. Fourthly, the danger of sepsis or of accidental infection, though of course this is extremely rare, is completely removed. Fifthly, these preparations are much less costly, and their use may be extended to those who cannot afford the expense of an autogenous hypodermic vaccine.

Up to the present time, although a certain amount of work has been done on acute disease with very promising results, attention has been mainly concentrated on all forms of chronic disease in which intestinal toxæmia has been wholly or in part the cause, and several hundreds of cases have been investigated. The relation to chronic disease of the non-lactose-fermenting organisms found in the intestinal content has now been so definitely established and accepted so universally by bacteriologists that no further comment on this point is necessary in this paper. The acceptance is of a two-fold nature: firstly, that these organisms play an enormous part in predisposing the patient to chronic disease of almost every form; secondly, that vaccines of these bacilli are valuable therapeutic agents and that great benefit has been obtained by their use. Suffice it to say that a vast amount of disease, heretofore considered hopeless, has been brought within the reach of cure.

The number of varieties of these non-lactose-fermenting bacilli is great – certainly amounting to thousands, if they are examined in minute detail according to the sugar reactions etc., but from the point of view of therapeutic administration of oral vaccines it is sufficient at the present time, at any rate, to divide them into seven main groups, classified according to their reactions on four sugars, as in the following table:

	GLUCOSE	LACTOSE	SACCHAROSE	DULCITE
Fæcalis alkaligenes	Alkaline	—	—	—
Dysentery type	Acid	—	—	—
Morgan type	Acid & gas	—	—	—
Gaertner type	Acid & gas	—	—	Acid & gas
Proteus type	Acid & gas	—	Acid & gas	—
Coli mutabile	Acid & gas	Late Acid & gas	—	—
No. 7 type	Acid & gas	—	Acid & gas	Acid & gas

For the purposes of treatment there are two requirements: (1) a bacteriological investigation to ascertain if the patient has an infection with any of the above types of organism, and (2) an autogenous vaccine, or the polyvalent vaccine of the particular group to which the infecting organism belongs.

To determine if any intestinal infection is present, the fæces of the patient are plated in the usual way, using McConkey's neutral-red-bile-salt-peptone-lactose agar. If white colonies are present, these are picked off and cultures made, which are tested on the four sugars, as shown in the table above, to ascertain into which of the seven groups they fall. It must be borne in mind that these abnormal organisms are not persistently present and that positive and negative phases occur, exactly as they do in the case of typhoid carriers, so it is often necessary to make daily examinations until a positive result is obtained. As a rule three or four examinations are sufficient, but occasionally it is necessary to continue for a few weeks; a longer time than three weeks is uncommon.

The method of preparation is as follows: an 18-hour incubated agar slope of the organism is washed up in 2 cc of distilled water, and the emulsion killed in the ordinary way in the water bath at 60° C., except that thirty minutes is sufficient, instead of the usual hour. 1 cc of this emulsion is added to 99 grammes of milk sugar in a mortar and the mixture is vigorously ground with a pestle for twenty minutes. The resulting powder is the first strength of the vaccine. 1 gramme of this powder is then added to 99 grammes of milk sugar and similarly ground for twenty minutes: this gives the second strength. 1 gramme of this is then added to 99 grammes of milk sugar and similarly ground to give the third strength, then 1 gramme is added to 99 cc of distilled water and vigorously shaken in a bottle; this gives the fourth strength. the process is continued by adding 1 cc of this mixture to 99 cc distilled water and again well shaking; and so on for any number of times, with repeated dilution and succussion.* The strengths which are most frequently used are the twelfth and the thirtieth.

For the preparation of a polyvalent vaccine it is necessary to obtain a large number of cultures of the particular group, keeping these until at least a hundred have accumulated, throughly mixing them, and then taking 1 cc of the mixture and treating it as above. Thus it is possible to have a powerful vaccine of each of the seven groups pure to strain.

METHOD OF DOSAGE

It has been found that with old people and debilitated subjects, or with cases where a definite reaction is undesirable, it is better to commence with a dose of the twelfth, but with the more vigorous it is quite safe to begin with the thirtieth strength. The dose consists of 3

---

*One-half or one-quarter of all these amounts may be taken, if found more convenient, provided the proportion is maintained.

or 4 drops taken from the stock bottle and added to 1 oz water; this should be given in two halves at four hours' interval, preferably before food. It is then essential to await the result, allowing at least three weeks to elapse before deciding that no benefit has been obtained. If any improvement occurs, no matter how slight, no further dose should be given under any conditions whatever as long as the least progress is being made, even though this may mean waiting weeks or months only repeating when the condition becomes definitely stationary, or there is a tendency to relapse.

ILLUSTRATIVE CASES

Case 1. Miss N.G. aet 35. Attacks started at six years of age, averaging one a week. Mother epileptic; father alcoholic. Bacteriological examination of fæces gave 20 per cent of an abnormal bacillus of the Morgan type.

October 28, 1927. First dose of twelfth strength. Improvement followed. No sign of any trouble for a period of almost six weeks, when a very mild attack occurred.

December 7th, 1927. Dose repeated.

February 6th, 1928. Very mild attack. Third dose given.

The case is still under observation. In all, twelve doses have been required in nearly two years, the last being given in May, 1929. There have been five definite attacks during that period the last one being on November 21, 1928. During 1929, the most serious symptoms have been slight giddiness and depression on four occasions.

Case 2, Mr J.L. aet 44. Chronic colitis of five years standing; frequent loose stools with much mucus exacerbations with attacks of diarrhoea every three or four weeks. General debility with marked depression and frequent headaches. Bacteriological examination of fæces gave 90 per cent of an abnormal bacillus of the proteus type.

June 22, 1928. First dose of thirtieth strength given. Rapid and marked improvement, with disappearance of all symptoms by the end of July. Patient remained well until March 1929, when there was a slight return of symptoms. The dose was repeated, again with rapid improvement, which has been maintained.

Case 3. Mr C.J. aet 50. Nervous breakdown due to overwork and business strain; marked depression and inability to concentrate, steadily increasing during one year; nervous dyspepsia, pain and flatulence following food. Bacteriological examination of fæces gave 5 per cent of an abnormal bacillus of the Morgan type.

August 8, 1927. First dose of thirtieth strength. Steady improvement, and by the middle of August patient able to resume light duties. Progress continued, and by the middle of September patient considered himself unusually well.

October 1, 1927. No further progress, so second dose given. Still further improvement, and condition better than for some years.

Owing to slight relapses four more doses were given during the next eight months, the last being on June 22, 1928. Since then there has been no necessity for any treatment.

Case 4. Mrs B. aet 62. Severe headaches, debility, and other symptoms of chronic renal disease. Blood pressure 232.

Examination of urine showed albumen and casts present.

Bacteriological examination of fæces gave 10 per cent of an abnormal bacillus of the fæcalis alkaligenes type.

January 3, 1928. First dose of twelfth strength. General improvement. Headaches less frequent and severe. Blood pressure fell to 209. Amount of albumen diminished.

February 4, 1928. Second dose given, as condition appeared stationary.

A further three doses were given in 1928, and two in 1929. The headaches have almost entirely disappeared since April, and the general health has been good, the blood pressure keeping about 200 and the percentage of albumen slight.

Case 5. Mrs C. aet 44. Very severe headaches for eight years, one a month, necessitating at least one day in bed.

Bacteriological examination of fæces gave 2 per cent of an abnormal bacillus of the Morgan type.

January 14, 1928. First dose of thirtieth strength.

The February attack was missed.

March 3, 1928. A mild attack necessitated a second dose.

Since then six further doses have been given, the last one being on April 19, 1929. For the last twelve months the attacks have been very mild and have now practically ceased.

It will readily be seen that the great advantages of this method of administration apply not only to the patient, but also to the physician, because once good stocks of polyvalent vaccine have been prepared, they are practically inexhaustible. Hence the cost is reduced, and the administration is easily carried out by any practitioner. The only necessary preliminary is a bacteriological examination to determine the type of the infecting organism.

So many medical men can now guarantee the efficacy of these preparations that all doubt as to their value has been removed. Hitherto hypodermic vaccines of these abnormal bacilli have very considerably increased our power of cure in cases of chronic disease, and now we have at our disposal an equally effective, but simpler method of treatment, which can be extended to those who have objections or prejudices to the hypodermic method.

Space forbids, in an article of this description, any discussion of the physical properties of these preparations, but the work of modern physicists is tending to show that certain properties are released and that very active substances are present in these dilutions.

This work is being further elaborated by Dr T.M. Dishington of Glasgow, who has spent several years in patient research on this subject, and it is hoped before long to be able to publish the symptoms peculiar to each particular group of organisms, so that prescribing will be possible on symptomatology alone, without any need of the laboratory.

It will be quite obvious to many of our readers that the method adopted in the preparation of these oral vaccines is identical with that used by the Homœopathic school for the past century in preparing their remedies, and the knowledge that bacteria so treated prove an invaluable therapeutic agent must form a link between the advanced school of Immunity of today and that of Homœopathy, which has existed for a hundred years. And although Homœopathy needs no support other than that given by the effective cures obtained through its science, this link must be of great value in demonstrating to members of the allopathic school the confirmation of one of Hahnemann's discoveries by this different point of view which has now been effected in the laboratory.

The Rediscovery of Psora

[*British Homœopathic Journal*, January 1929]

The object of this paper* is to continue the discussion of the problems presented to you by Dr Dishington at your last meeting on certain nosodes prepared from abnormal organisms in the intestinal canal, which have been brought before your notice on different occasions during the past eight years. I want to describe to you how these nosodes have been developed and evolved, and the processes of thought, reasoning and practice which have placed them in the position they now hold.

Three main principles had to be realized before the present effective state of these nosodes could be obtained: (1) The discovery of the group of bacilli which formed their basis; (2) the value of Hahnemann's laws with regard to repetition in the application of the doses; and (3) the fact that the nosodes would be effective in a potentized state.

About 1912 it was recognized that there were to be found in the intestinal content of both apparently healthy as well as diseased people a class of bacilli which had hitherto been considered unimportant, but which were then proved to be associated with chronic disease. These organisms were the various types of non-lactose-fermenting bacilli belonging to the great coli-typhoid group, very closely allied to such organisms as the typhoids, dysenteries and paratyphoids, yet not giving rise to acute disease and, in fact, not associated with any specific morbid conditions. Since there was not this connection, they had in the past been regarded as of no importance, and had been disregarded by bacteriologists and clinicians. About this time, owing to the frequency with which these bacilli were found to be present in such a large percentage of cases when no other

*Read to the *British Homœopathic Society* on November 1, 1928.

abnormal or pathogenic organisms could be isolated, it was decided to try the use of these in vaccines to see if any benefit could be obtained in cases of chronic disease, and it was found that in spite of them being non-pathogenic in the ordinary sense of the word, great benefit could be obtained when they were used as a therapeutic agent in this manner. It was shown that by such vaccines a mild exacerbation of all the symptoms in a chronic case could be produced, and that in favourable circumstances a definite improvement followed. Cases of good results were recorded when patients were so treated, but in those days the percentage of these was comparatively small, owing to the fact that the injections were given much too frequently and a stated intervals, such as a week or ten days, with a consequent result of serious over-dosing and interference with the starting of a beneficial reaction. At the present time several bacteriologists and a considerable number of clinicians can testify to the undoubted connection that exists between these organisms and chronic disorders and between them and intestinal toxæmia with its consequent morbid results, so that there no longer remains the least doubt as regards this relationship. Some hundreds of practitioners have proved this point from the clinical results that have been obtained by the use of preparations made from these organisms, and the evidence has now grown so large that there is no longer any room for doubt on this point. A certain amount of laboratory evidence has also been accumulated to prove that there is a relationship between these groups of organisms and disease. If specimens of a patient are plated out day by day for a considerable period, it will be found that these abnormal organisms which are the subject of this paper are not persistently and constantly present, but that there are negative phases when they are entirely absent, and positive ones when they are present in varying proportions. Moreover, the total numbers during the positive phases vary from day to day. If we start plating during a negative phase, after a time they begin to appear in the specimens, at first in small numbers, then steadily rising each day until the maximum is reached, when the percentage again falls until they disappear. Both the maximum percentage and the length of the positive and negative phases may vary very considerably in different subjects, but the interesting point is that the health of the individual, whether in disease or in an apparently normal condition, varies directly with these phases. Most commonly in cases of chronic illness the symptoms are worse towards the end of the negative period and are relieved when there is an output of the abnormal organisms, and generally speaking the greater the output the more benefit the patient receives. In the apparently healthy if there are any times when the individual tends to be below the normal standard and is not up to his usual form, these generally occur at the same period of the cycle. Boyd and Paterson in Glasgow are proving further points of relationship between these states and the condition of the patient.

The result of a vaccine is usually to cause a greater and more prolonged output to the benefit of the patient. If daily charts of the results of the examinations are kept, it is generally possible to know from these the condition of the patients and how they are progressing, and they have very often been a useful guide in selecting the correct time for the repetition of doses. Thus, from a clinical and a laboratory standpoint, there can no longer be any doubt that these groups of organisms bear a distinct relationship to chronic disease.

The next step – the discovery that the doses should be given not at stated intervals, but according to the response of the patient – came as follows. In the laboratories at University College, in treating cases of pneumonia with vaccine, it was found that better results were obtained when doses were given according to how the patient reacted to the injection, and that if after a dose the pulse rate and temperature fell, the results were much more satisfactory if no further treatment was given as long as this improvement continued, repetition only being made when the pulse-rate and temperature tended again to rise. The cures occurred more quickly and with a higher percentage of successful results, and considerably fewer doses of vaccine were required. After this had been definitely realized and proved, it logically followed to try the same method with all types of acute febrile cases, and the same beneficial results were found to occur. When this had been definitely established, it occurred to the same workers that this law which appeared to apply to all acute diseases might possibly be the same for cases of a chronic type. So it was tried, and the results again were more than had been anticipated.

In chronic cases a minimum interval of three weeks was allowed to elapse before a dose was repeated, because it was found that in some instances benefit did not begin much before that time, and if at the end of three weeks improvement had started no further dose was given until every trace of improvement had ceased, and that either the condition had become stationary or there was a tendency to relapse. On these lines it was found that the period of amelioration varied in cases from two or three weeks to intervals as long, in rare examples, as twelve months, and that by refusing to repeat during the time of improvement enormously better results were obtained and a higher percentage of good results occurred, while of course a much smaller amount of vaccine in each case had to be given. Such was the success that this method has been persevered with up to the present time.

At this stage, therefore, we had arrived at two conclusions: (1) That this particular group of non-pathogenic non-lactose-fermenting bacilli of the intestine were undoubtedly associated with chronic disease, and (2) that vaccines made from them were very valuable curative agents, if given according to the laws of Hahnemann and studying the response of the patient, and not, as had hitherto been done, at regular intervals.

It was at this stage that, coming to your hospital as your bacteriologist, one was introduced to the science of homœopathy. On reading Hahnemann's *Organon* for the first time one instantly realized the fact that the work of the modern immunity school was merely the rediscovery, by a different method, of facts that had been realized by him a century before, and in conjunction with some of your physicians homœopathic principles were at once applied to these various groups of bacilli and preparations made from them, potentizing them in the same way as you do your remedies. It required only a very short time to prove that nosodes so prepared were of very great therapeutic value, and the further research of the last eight years, in which many hundreds of cases were treated, has more than justified the earlier hopes. Today, not only in England, but to an even greater extent in Germany and America, and also to a lesser extent in France, Holland and Switzerland, these nosodes are being used.

Looking at it from the homœopathic point of view, the first important point to be considered is whether these preparations are in accordance with the laws of Hahnemann and whether it is an extension of his work. Many of us feel that this is the case, as the founder of homœopathy in more than one instance uses the morbid product of disease as the basis of a remedy, and one has little doubt that if he had been in a position to isolate these organs they would have been used. Moreover, it is still uncertain whether these organisms are the cause, the result or an attempted cure of disease. We can do little more at the present time than say that there is an association, but its exact nature it is impossible as yet to determine. It is not at all improbable that these bacilli are a variation of the *Bacillus coli* and the latter, from its universal presence in our modern civilization, not only in men, but in animals, birds, &c, must be considered more or less as a normal inhabitant of the intestine. Experiments tend to indicate that during great basic fundamental changes in the body the intestinal flora may alter, as if attempting to keep in harmony, for it is not impossible that these groups of bacilli are the normal *B. coli* altered to meet certain needs, compelled to do so by the altered state of the host, and that when the bacteria are in this condition they are undoubtedly valuable therapeutic agents when potentized. Science is tending to show that life is harmony – a state of being in tune – and that disease is discord or a condition when a part of the whole is not vibrating in unison.

In a differentiation of these organisms it is interesting to note that the sugar lactose is used. Lactose differs from the rest of the sugars in that it is an animal product, the others being vegetable. Recent research indicates that for a ferment to be able to act upon a substance, the ferment must be able to vibrate in tune with the atomic weight of the substance which has to be fermented. Hence, it means that organisms capable of fermenting lactose are able to vibrate in tune with animal tissue, whilst those which are unable to do this are equally unable to be in harmony with substances other than of the vegetable type. If this theory is able to stand the test of time, it will get us a considerable way towards the understanding of things of fundamental nature, and it means that we have here a method of differentiating organisms which are benficent from those which are adverse to the human subject. It is at such a time as they are adverse that we choose to potentize these products and use them as therapeutic agents in the cure of disease. On all other points, of course, the nosodes are identical with homœopathic remedies, and their preparation is exactly in accordance with the laws of materia medica.

No one who has studied intestinal toxæmia to any extent can possibly fail to see the similarity between this and the basic, fundamental disease described by Hahnemann as psora. I am not going into this in detail today, because I understand that Dr Gordon, of Edinburgh, is going to draw this similarity for you at length at some future date, when he will point out to you the indubitable provings of the nature of intestinal toxæmia which Hahnemann classified under the name of psora.

There is one point of interest which I may mention here in relation to this point, namely, that Hahnemann lays great stress on the impossibility of having more than one disease at the same time. This we find in regard to the work on intestinal flora; it is surprising that only in the very rarest cases does one find more than one abnormal type of organism present in one individual, another point of confirmation of the theory that the two states are identical.

In spite of there only being one type of organism present at a particular period, this type may certainly be changed by means of a vaccine, or nosode, or remedy administration, indicating that the type of organism depends on the condition of the patient, and that it varies its nature in conformity with the soil in which it has to live. Generally speaking, in people who have not been treated by homœopathic methods, the organism remains much more constant to its type over a prolonged period of time.

The next point which has to be emphasized is the extent to which the allopathic school are at the present time adopting homœopathic methods. Quite apart from the work of which I have been speaking this evening concerning these nosodes, which are being used by quite a large number of allopaths in different parts of the world, most of whom have been more or less instructed in the proper principles of repetition, so that no harm is likely to be experienced on that score. There is another school which has quite independently worked out the administration of oral vaccines and is now on a large scale using low potencies of these and giving them by mouth. So far these workers, who are now represented in every country in the world, have not used dilutions above the 4x. During the past few years Besredka and others have done an enormous amount of work proving the efficacy of giving vaccines by mouth, both as prophylaxis against and also as a cure of disease. Large numbers of experiments have shown that animals can be rendered immune against live organisms to which they are very susceptible by a few doses of dead emulsion of the same bacteria given by mouth. Moreover, tests done among troops have very hopeful results as to the power of the same preparations to protect against infection from typhoid, dysentery, &c, in ordinary life, so that at the present time, both for prophylaxis and treatment, the oral vaccine is becoming an established factor and firms are engaged not only in this country, but on a much greater scale on the Continent, in the manufacture of these preparations in large quantities. The suspensions are not potentized in the full sense of the word, but owing to the minuteness of bacteria the total quantity present is very small indeed and probably corresponds to about a 2x or 3x of a homœopathic remedy; hence they are very closely allied to your potencies. This work, which is rapidly growing and extending, comes of course entirely from the allopathic school and has no connection with homœopathy. It has been developed quite independently through scientific laboratories of the old school. Unconsciously, again, Hahnemann's work is being rediscovered, and a vast number of remedies prepared, though only in low potencies. An attempt is being made by the old school to form a complete materia medica, using as their base the various types of organisms, of which of course there are very numerous varieties.

To give you an example, the following is a quotation from the quarterly bulletin of one of our leading firms:

"The vaccine-therapist claims a multiple variety of cases in which the use of vaccines by subcutaneous injection is beneficial. One must admit, however, that there are many conditions in which the administration of vaccine by injection is contra-indicated. Acute febrile cases and nervous patients who are hypersensitive may be mentioned as the more important examples.

"It is not generally known that in staphylococcal and streptococcal infections oral vaccines, administered by the mouth in the same way as ordinary medicines, are equally if not more effective than vaccines given by injection. Frequent visits for injections are unnecessary as the patient can easily take the oral vaccines at home at the times ordered by the practitioner. In the treatment of boils and carbuncles some striking successes have been obtained."

Another aspect which it is necessary for every homœpath to understand is what Hahnemann realized well enough – the incompleteness of materia medica and the fact that it could not cover all existing diseases. Moreover, he saw that new illness might arise owing to altering circumstances of civilization, and that new remedies would have to be sought. Again, his genius comprehended the fact that in

Nature might be found an infinite number of remedies to meet all occasions that might arise. The following paragraphs quoted from the *Organon* will show you his realization of the necessity for more remedies, and the enormous amount of work that must be done by his followers to improve on his original findings to keep pace with disease in its ever-varying characteristics:

> "Since the number of medicines exactly tested in regard to their positive action is as yet only moderate, it sometimes happens that only a smaller or greater part of the symptoms of a case of disease can be found in the symptom-register of the most suitable medicine. Consequently this incomplete counter-disease force must be employed for a lack of a complete one" (para 133).

> "If the drug first chosen actually corresponds to the disease in its entirety, it must cure it. But if, owing to the insufficient number of fully proved drugs and the consequent restriction of our choice, the medicine selected is not exactly homœopathic, then it will arouse new symptoms which will in their turn point the way to the next remedy likely to prove serviceable" (para 184).

> "Truly only a considerable supply of medicines thus accurately known in their positive modes of action can serve our turn, and enable us to discover a remedy for every one of the innumerable natural cases of disease.

> "When thousands of exact and tireless observers, instead of one as hitherto, have laboured at the discovery of these first elements of a rational materia medica, what will it not be possible to effect in the whole extent of the endless kingdom of disease! Then the art of medicine will no longer he mocked at as an art of conjecture lacking all foundation" (para 122).

Then again, his realization of the enormous possibilities in the variety of disease is illustrated in the following:

> "Every epidemic or sporadic collective disease is to be regarded and treated as a nameless, individual disorder, which has never occurred before exactly as in this case, in this person and in these circumstances, and can never in this identical form appear in the world again" (para 60).

"Every disease epidemic in the world differs from every other, excepting only those few which are caused by a definite unchangeable miasm. Further, even every single case of epidemic and sporadic disease differs from every other, those only excepted that belong to the collective disease noted elsewhere. Therefore the rational physician will judge every case of illness brought under his care according to its individual characteristics. When he has investigated its individual features and noted all its signs and symptoms (for they exist in order to be noted) he will treat it according to its individuality (i.e. according to the particular group of symptoms it displays), with a suitable individual remedy" (para 48).

The last point on which one wants to lay stress is that Hahnemann also visualized the inexhaustible supply of remedies if only efforts were taken to obtain them. Quoting from him again:

"On the other hand, the disease-producing powers usually termed 'drugs' or 'medicines' can be used for purposes of cure, with infinitely greater ease, far more certainty and with a range of choice almost unlimited; we can give to the counter-disease thereby aroused (which is to remove the natural disease that we are called to treat) a regulated strength and duration, because the size and weight of the dose lie at our command; and as every medicine differs from every other and possesses a wide range of action, we have in the great multitude of drugs an unlimited number of artificial diseases ready to hand, which we can oppose with decisive choice to the natural course of the diseases and infirmities of mankind, and so, swiftly and surely, remove and extinguish natural disorders by means of very similar diseases artificially produced." (para 37)

There is no doubt that these nosodes are going to play a large part in the future treatment of disease, and if they are essentially homœopathic they ought to be distributed to the world through homœopathic channels for two reasons: (1) That any extensions of Hahnemann's work should be added to that of his which already exists as a natural respect to his genius; (2) a point of far greater importance, these nosodes can only be a perfect success when combined with other homœopathic treatment. It must not be forgotten that these nosodes probably only represent one branch of disease, that included by

Hahnemann under the name of psora, and that as a part their action is limited and restricted to a certain phase in the treatment of disease, and cannot be expected under any conditions to cover anything like the whole picture. Therefore, the successful prescriber must also have at his command all other remedies which are at present in the Pharmacopœia or which may in the future be added to it, so that he may be able to deal with the totality of any one or more cases, and whilst the allopathic school is perfectly willing to accept nosodes, or, as they are called, oral vaccines, of bacteria of all forms, it limits the new pharmacopœia to this region of remedies, and will not have the benefit of the hundred years of experience of all the various herbs and natural remedies so completely tested out by your school.

These nosodes may be looked upon as great cleaning powers improving the condition of a patient and in certain cases effecting a complete cure, in others so cleaning up the whole state that the patient, who before gave no response, now receives marked benefit from other remedies. Again, the fundamental factor in using this treatment is the very careful repetition of the doses entirely according to the response of the patient, a law with which all homœopaths are familiar but which it will take a long time for allopaths to appreciate. If these nosodes are launched on the profession through the allopathic world, their chance of success is very small in comparison with what it might be if contracted through your channels, because of these two points, the lack of the complete materia medica and the at present comparatively unknown law of the correct repetition of doses.

Such has been the success of the practical results of these preparations, that already more allopaths have used them than there are homœopaths on the Register in England; some of them have entirely discarded the syringe and the old hypodermic method of injection for the use of the nosode, and one can see a distinct danger ahead if this practice spreads too widely without the control of a ruling body, as it should be used only by men who have had distinct training. The existence of homœopathy in this country depends to an extent on its ability to cure cases where allopathy has failed, and the possession of these preparations enables the allopath who uses them properly to complete to a much more considerable extent than previously, and you can be sure that if this work is taken up by the other school and the proper interval between doses acknowledged, it will be claimed by them as entirely their own discovery. You have today in Dr Paterson, of Glasgow, your own pathologist working on these nosodes, preparing them and actually doing further research on the subject, so that you are from an internal source proceeding with the work.

In conclusion, I want to remind you of paragraphs which ended a paper I read to you in April, 1920, which are as follows:

"Meanwhile it should be realized that science in a totally different manner is confirming the principles of homœopathy. To Hahnemann should fall all the honour for having anticipated science by more than a century.

"The attitude today of the medical profession in general is one of regard towards homœopathy; but when, as is shortly certain to happen, it is generally recognized and appreciated that all modern research at the hands of allopaths is rapidly proving and drifting in the direction of Hahnemann's laws, then will homœopathy be acknowledged to be the wonderful science that it is.

"Let all the members of your Society see to it that they are proud to be amongst the pioneers; let them see to it that they do not err one jot from the fundamental laws of their great founder. For science is proving him in detail – the like remedy, the single dose, the danger of hasty repetition.

"It is going to be a struggle between the old homœopathy and the new; see to it that the old receives its due share of credit, that its standard is kept high, and that, true to its teachings, it is not swamped in the flood of science which is merely following in the wake of Hahnemann."

I wish it were possible that we could present to you seven herbs instead of seven groups of bacteria, because there always seems to be some reticence in the minds of many to use anything associated with disease in the treatment of pathological conditions. Possibly this is a narrow-minded outlook, and in this age we are too inclined to want to keep medicine perfectly pure and have swung a little to the opposite extreme, possibly as reaction from the practices of the Middle Ages and the vivisection of today. Moreover, it may be that the organisms we are using are beneficent to mankind and not adverse.

We are making every endeavour to replace the bacterial nosode by means of plants and have, in fact, matched some of them almost exactly; for example, ornithogalum in its vibrations is almost identical with the Morgan group, and we have discovered a seaweed which has almost all the properties of the dysentery type, but there is yet one thing lacking, and that one point keeps us checkmated in the effort to avoid using bacterial nosodes. This vital point is polarity. The remedies of the meadow and of Nature, when potentized, are of positive polarity, whereas those which have been associated with disease are of the reverse type, and at the present time it seems that it is this reversed polarity which is so essential in the results which are being obtained by bacterial nosodes. Perhaps at some future date a new form of potentizing may be discovered, which will be capable of reversing the polarity of the simple elements and plants, but until that time comes we have no alternative.

The beneficial effect of these nosodes is now accepted internationally, and the daily amount of good which is being accomplished in the fight against disease is on an enormous scale, so that it does not seem that this benefit should be withheld from humanity until such time as we may have found a particular method of combating the psora of Hahnemann by a means which will fit in with the æsthetic mentality of the most fastidious type. Infinitely more important it is that this work should be acknowledged as a continuation of that of Hahnemann and, though not in itself perfect, as leading the way to further discovery. Its growth and development should be watched and directed by the homœopathic school, and not be allowed to fall into abuse in the hands of men who do not understand the fundamental principles on which it is established.

– XVII –

The Problem of Chronic Disease

[Paper read at the International Homœopathic
Congress, 1927]

From the earliest records of medical history we find evidence that
what we know today as intestinal toxæmia was consciously or unconsciously recognized, as evidenced by the drugs and remedies used by
the earliest physicians, many of which were laxative and liver stimulating and hence intestinal cleansing in their effect. Throughout the
ages of medical science similar efforts by different methods have been
attempted, and even today much of modern treatment by diet, drugs,
and even surgery is based on similar conceptions.

The alimentary canal must of necessity be of the utmost importance. Its superficial area is greater than that of the skin surface of our
bodies; moreover, it has the power of absorbing from that in which it
is bathed – a property not possessed by our external surface in any
similar degree; you may sit in a bath of potassium cyanide with no
ill-effects, a very small amount of which would be fatal in the stomach; you may wash in water loaded with typhoid or diphtheria or
other bacilli without harm, but if a microscopical amount enters the
mouth the result may be serious or fatal.

The content of the tract is the fluid in which we live; from which we
obtain our fluid and our food; it is to us similar to the water in which
the unicellular amœbæ moves. It is essential that it should be pure and
contain the necessaries of life, and free from any substances which if
absorbed may be harmful to the body and against which there is no
protective mechanism.

It is surely one of the marvels of Nature that she has been able to
cope with such diversity of intestinal content as that with which
different races have tested her powers of adaptation. Consider the
varying diets of different countries; think of the vastly varied composition of the intestinal content as a result; and yet the races, generally

speaking, survive. As yet the penalty is not death – merely disease; not extinction – merely degeneration.

In all probability the human race was originally intended to live on raw material, the fruits and foods of the tropics, and the human alimentary canal was evolved to deal with such a diet; yet offshoots of that race have migrated to temperate climes and many nations live almost entirely on food which has been cooked, completely altering the intestinal content – and yet the race survives; but humanity does not escape entirely. It may live, but it suffers; it suffers from a hundred and one diseases, from a lowered standard of health and strength and a loss of physical vitality.

It is against all probability that human nature will for some time if ever retrace its steps and return to a primitive condition, and even if that ultimately is the result it does not concern us; we are interested in those countless millions of this, our age, and the age of the near future, who will demand to live as we do today and yet cry aloud for health and relief from suffering. We have to meet present needs, not stand idly waiting for an ideal future.

When a race lives on unnatural food, the intestinal content changes chemically, physically and bacteriologically. All these factors matter, but in people such as those with which we are dealing the bacteriological change matters most.

The chemical and physical characters can be brought somewhat within range of normal by a diet not too far removed from that of civilization by the addition of fruit, salad, &c., and by such means the extreme variance from the normal in both the chemical and physical condition can be remedied even within the limits of diets which are not incompatible with the modern possibilities of private home and public restaurants. I mean that it is possible to lunch and dine daily at many restaurants and select such food as will keep the intestine reasonably clean without being considered mentally deranged or even very exceptional. But although this may be accomplished it does not of necessity follow that it is in itself sufficient to cure disease.

In a few cases it may be so, but where there has been an infection of long standing, or where the infection is deeply seated, the bacterial element will resist for at any rate a long time the improvement in the intestinal content, and other methods have to be devised to hasten its removal; hence the greater importance of the bacterial infection as opposed to the abnormal chemical and physical state, owing to the greater difficulty in correction.

Has it ever occurred to you what difference there is between the content of the large intestine of an individual living on raw food and one living on cooked food?

In the latter instance such as is met with in civilized people the content is foul in odour, dark in colour, alkaline in reaction; containing many products of putrefaction such as indol, and the bacterial content is composed of *Bacillus coli*, streptococci and spore-bearing organisms. Contrast this with the healthy individual who lives on raw material.

The large intestinal content is of no odour, light in colour, acid in reaction; free from putrefactive products, and the bacterial content consists of the lactic acid bacilli together with some *Bacillus coli*.

To any conversant with this contrast it is in itself grounds for serious thought.

In many cases cure can be accomplished without alteration of even an unnatural diet, where no amount of dieting would give marked benefit, though I do not deny that the combination would be better and more lasting.

The essential point about a suitable diet is that whilst supplying the needs of the body it should tend to keep the reaction of the large intestine slightly acid – instead of alkaline, as is much more usual in western civilization. The acidity depends on the growth of the lactic acid bacillus, and this organism, again, needs the presence of starch to ensure its multiplication. Ordinary forms of starch are converted to sugar long before the colon is reached, but uncooked oatmeal, or better still, crushed nuts, are convenient means of supplying a starch that remains largely unconverted to sugar in the upper part of the bowel.

I do not feel that it is yet proven that the class of bacteria which is the subject of this paper are the cause of disease. I am not certain. They may be the result, but I do maintain that this group of organisms of which I am about to speak are persistent in patients; that they are associated with chronic disease, and that by the use of preparations made from these bacteria themselves we have a most powerful weapon in the fight against chronic disease of all types.

I turn now to the consideration of these organisms, indicators of potential, if not of present, disease whenever they are found, and found they can be in the vast majority of our fellow citizens. It may be asked why, if they are so deadly, is disease not always demonstrable? The answer is that their immediate virulence is small, and bodies that start with a reasonable measure of health can face their toxins for years without apparent inconvenience. But as life advances with all its various stresses the strain of keeping back these organisms, or possibly the conditions which give rise to them, begins to tell, and presently there is a breach in the defences and obvious illness declares itself. It is because a breakdown can normally be deferred until middle age, when the next generation is launched, that resistance to these organisms is not a very active power, for it remains often true that Nature, if careful of the type, is careless of the single life. In a similar way the long latent period of tuberculosis led to the belief held for many years that it was not infective.

The germs of which I speak are bacilli – Gram-negative, of the great coli typhoid group; the important point being that they are incapable of fermenting lactose – a point which distinguishes them from the *Bacillus coli* itself.

They are not pathogenic in the ordinary sense, as are the typhoid or dysentery or paratyphoid bacilli, and have in the past been mostly regarded as of no importance. They are not identical with but closely allied to these organisms, and belong to their class.

Their number is probably enormous, possibly infinite. It is possible to investigate a hundred without obtaining two identical strains.

We can, however, put them into groups, though even this is relatively a crude classification, as it must be understood that each group contains a host of varieties, differing from one another in some minute detail.

For the purpose of this work these non-lactose fermenting bacilli have been attached to one of six groups, namely:

Dysentery
Gaertner
Fœcalis alkaligenes
Morgan
Proteus
Coli mutabile

They are grouped according to their powers of fermenting certain sugars, and only a few sugars have been used so as to keep the number of groups small. If an autogenous vaccine is used the exact definition of the organism is of no importance for treatment, and the polyvalent throws a very wide net and contains many representatives of each class.

These, then, are the bacilli which for the most part are considered harmless, but which are really the indication and, if properly used, a means of cure of chronic disease.

The clinical evidence of the power to cure is too well established to admit of doubt, and will be referred to presently, but the laboratory is accumulating evidence of a non-clinical nature which demonstrates the connection between these organisms and disease.

By daily examinations of the fæces of a patient it is possible, by recording the percentage of organisms present in the form of a chart, to show the relation between the condition of the patient and the percentage found.

By percentage I mean the ratio between the abnormal non-lactose-fermenting organisms and the number of *Bacillus coli* present. Generally speaking, it is considered normal for coli alone to be present, but these abnormal bacilli may be found in anything from 1 to 100 per cent of the total colonies obtained.

From the alteration in percentage during treatment it can be ascertained to a certain degree how well a patient is likely to respond.

As a general rule the organisms found remain true to type for any given case. That is to say, Gaertner does not seem to change to a Morgan or a proteus.

If a patient's fæces are plated daily and the percentage of abnormal bacilli charted, it will be found that these are not uniformly present, but that they occur in cycles. Perhaps for a period the specimens are free, and then the organisms appear, rapidly rise in numbers, remain at the highest point for some time, and then diminish until they disappear.

The intervals of freedom from them, the periods of the positive phase of their presence, the highest percentage of them reached, vary in different cases, but the clinical condition of the patient bears a certain relationship to the curve of organisms present in the specimens.

This relationship is not yet sufficiently worked out to lay down definite laws, as more than one type of curve exists; but I can assure you there is a definite relation between clinical conditions and bacterial percentage, and as an example of this the most brilliant result after vaccine treatment occurs when there is a short negative phase followed by a higher and more prolonged positive phase than that which is the patient's usual routine. Generally speaking, those cases where there is little or no alteration from their usual type of course do not do so well.

Much work has still to be done on these lines and it will lead to a profitable result.

It is extraordinary how rapidly the bacterial content may alter. Perhaps after weeks of negative plating, within thirty-six hours the specimens may contain as high as 100 per cent of these abnormal bacilli.

What happens to produce this result we do not yet know; whether these organisms kill off the normal coli, whether the coli become altered to the abnormal type, whether it is a changed condition of the intestinal content or of the patient himself that causes this change gives room for much research, and when that problem is solved we shall have made a great advance towards the knowledge of the cause of disease.

But whatever may be the explanation, it is already established that the percentage of these bacilli in the specimens bears a direct relation towards the condition of the patient in his varying phases from a clinical point of view.

Another curious feature is the stability of a particular type of bacillus in a given subject, to which I have already alluded. Over several years, no matter how often examinations be made and whatever the condition or disease of the patient, the particular type remains true. Moreover, it is rare to find more than one type in the same case, although this may happen in a small percentage.

There are certain symptoms which occur more frequently with one type than with another, and it is not improbable, when further observations are made, that it will be found there is a close relationship between certain disease symptoms and definite types of these organisms.

Whether these organisms be the cause or result, they are associated with chronic disease, and an enormous amount of benefit can be obtained by the use of vaccine made from them. This has certainly been proven conclusively during the last twelve years.

I have previously referred to the fact that the clinical evidence of the value of this method of treatment is sufficient to leave no room for doubt. That statement must be justified.

Hundreds and thousands of patients have been treated on these lines, by a considerable number of practitioners; by both hypodermic and potentized preparations. Eighty per cent of those patients have shown improvement (to place it at a moderate figure), some only a little benefit, the majority very definite relief, a good many brilliant results and about 10 per cent practically miracles.

It is not without years of experience and experiments, not without the observation of thousands of cases, that I place this proposition before you; not without the co-operation and observation and experience of practitioners throughout the British Isles, who will support this evidence.

Patients may be treated with vaccines of these organisms given by hypodermic injection, as has been done now for a considerable number of years. This does not concern us today, but I may refer you to our book, *Chronic Disease*, for details.

The point I wish to stress is that as good, and I and others believe better, results are obtained by potentized preparations of killed organisms.

These have been in use for about seven years, and extensively for the last two years, by homœopaths and allopaths alike, and there are allopaths who have discarded the syringe for their use.

These potencies may be of two varieties, autogenous and polyvalent. I want to make this point quite clear.

An autogenous preparation means that the bacillus of a particular patient is potentized and used for that patient.

A polyvalent implies collecting organisms from some hundreds of patients, mixing together and potentizing the whole. It is this preparation which has been submitted to you on previous occasions, as a nosode worthy of your consideration.

The autogenous is of use only for the subject from whom it was prepared, or possibly any patient having an identical infection. The polyvalent, on the other hand, is prepared with the object of covering as many cases as possible.

Of the relative merits of the two more experience is yet necessary before we can draw definite conclusions, but that is not of the utmost importance at this point, because even if the autogenous should be shown to give a higher percentage of good results, the polyvalent variety is so successful as to be a nosode worthy of consideration as an additional nosode for the homœopathic materia medica, and the results obtained by any who try this will be sufficiently good (I can say with confidence) that if it ever fails they would probably be stimulated at least to try the autogenous, and thus comparative experience will accumulate in a sufficient degree to be able to draw conclusions.

Work is being done on this subject at the present time, but it will be some time before a definite statement can be made. It is hoped that by various tests it will be possible to ascertain whether the polyvalent, autogenous, or even a mixture of two or three strains, will be the perfect form of administration for any particular patient.

It is necessary that I should delay you for a moment, that this paper may be complete, to give you the exact technical details of preparation so that any competent bacteriologist can prepare these potencies.

Fæces are plated on McConkey's ribipel agar, incubated sixteen hours. When this is done organisms grow as red or white colonies. If they ferment lactose with the production of acid, that acid reacts on the neutral red in the medium to give a red colony; if they be non-lactose fermenters no acid is formed, no action on the neutral red and the colonies grow white. Hence the only interest is in those colonies which after incubation are white in colour.

Cultures made from white colonies, rejecting the coloured, on agar slopes, incubated fifteen hours and sugar reactions determined to group the organisms.

One culture washed up in 2 cc distilled water

Sealed and killed at 60° C. for thirty minutes.

Triturated with milk sugar, the whole in 9 or the whole in 99 grm of milk sugar.

This makes 1st decimal or 1st centesimal potency, according to the amount of milk sugar used. Further potencies are made by trituration up to the 6th c or the 12th x, and thereafter with the usual fluid mediums.

Special care is necessary in sterilizing all apparatus used to free them of a previous potency. Dry heat of at least 140° C. for 15 minutes is probably more effective than steam or moist heat.

The polyvalent nosode is obtained by collecting cultures from several hundreds of cases; by adding them as they are obtained to a sterile bottle, and when a sufficient number have been reached 1 cc of the whole well mixed and shaken is potentized as above.

As far as my knowledge goes there is nothing in this nosode contrary to the laws of Hahnemann, and as a single remedy I believe it is more comprehensive than any other single one known.

It is a link between the allopathic and homœopathic schools; discovered by a member of the allopathic vanguard, it is found to be in line with homœopathic principles.

I submit this nosode to you as a remedy worth including in your pharmacopœia; useful especially as a basic remedy in cases which fail to respond to ordinary drugs, or where no remedy is especially indicated, though its use need not be restricted to these cases.

Much work has yet to be done; experiments are now being conducted to attempt to find whether these organisms are the cause or effect of the patient's condition.

The nosode I submit to you is being tried in both America and Germany, and in this country it is being used by a considerably larger number of allopaths than homœopaths. Some of the former, who for years have been getting good results with the hypodermic variety of the vaccine, have completely discarded the syringe in favour of the potency.

I believe that the proper use of this nosode is to regard it as a basic remedy, and I have no doubt that the most brilliant results will be obtained when it is followed by homœopathic treatment, matching the symptoms with the appropriate remedy.

The nosode is capable of removing a greater or less amount of a really profound basic trouble. It, so to speak, purifies the patients and tends to clean them up until they clearly express one simillimum, and renders them much more responsive to their remedy. Hence, brilliant though the results are which have been obtained by allopaths, in your hands they should be even better.

I appeal to you to give the nosode a trial, to use it on cases who have failed under other treatment and in those cases where a remedy is not clearly indicated. I can speak with confidence that you have only to give it a trial to find it very valuable.

I am not laying too much stress on the autogenous because I know that the polyvalent as a nosode will appeal to you more readily. In the case of giving vaccines hypodermically it is almost essential to have an autogenous to get the best results; here 95 per cent of the patients do much better on their own vaccine and only about 5 per cent respond more definitely to the polyvalent; but in the case of this potentized variety it is yet too early to make any such claim, and such is the success of the polyvalent that I am inclined to think in some cases it is better than, and in a large majority of cases equally as good, as the autogenous, though there probably will be always certain cases that will only respond to a personal nosode prepared from their own organisms.

The nosode, the remedy prepared from the material of disease, antedated bacteriology and the vaccine; but the relation of the latter to the former is obvious. To your school, pioneers in the clinical use of disease to cure disease, I offer a remedy which is, I believe, potent against the deepest of all diseases, that chronic toxæmia which the genius of Hahnemann divined and named. If I believe that I can make its nature clearer than was possible for him, I take no jot from his glory – rather I believe I am confirming and extending his work, and so paying him the only homage he would desire.

— XVIII —

Intestinal Toxæmia in its Relation to Cancer

[*British Homœopathic Journal*, October 1924]

This is a paper on intestinal toxæmia, in its relation to diseases, not excepting malignancy, and I hope that the points that I shall put before you may not only be of interest, but worthy of your consideration.

Intestinal toxæmia is no new subject. For the past hundred years an enormous amount of work has been expended upon it, both medically and surgically, in an effort to counter its ill effects, and even back to the early days of our profession we find treatment and drugs which had as their object, their one and main object, the cleansing of the bowel. But as the importance of this condition is being recognized, and as further work is being done, so we are better able to understand the details of its nature and the more exact conditions by which it obtains its deleterious results. The powerful and far-reaching effects of intestinal toxæmia are as yet only beginning to be understood. Its wholesale ravages upon civilization, ravages the more difficult to understand because of its insidious nature, have yet to be realized. The sure, steady lowering of resistance, and the predisposition to disease, and the benefits that accrue from its removal, in the vast majority of all diseases, is yet to be appreciated by the profession.

The primary cause of this abnormality is essentially diet, and secondly, infection, which is able to take place only through incorrect food, and in this paper I am going to attempt to give you some scientific and practical reasons, and show how important a part these play in most diseases and that the predisposing causes of cancer are no exception.

Food is the fuel of the human engine, supplying the need of every minute cell of that most wonderful of all machines, the human body. But, as I shall show, if the fuel is deficient in its necessary characters, it not only becomes a source of diminished energy, but allows another host of possibilities in the production of poisons and deleterious substances fatal to the perfect working of the individual. We have had cranks and theorists throughout all time debating the varied value of different foods, and any who deviate from the custom of their particular society are considered eccentric. I am hoping to relate to you today the beginning of research whose further advance will demonstrate accurately the correct and normal diet for the human subject.

There cannot be the least doubt that civilized diet is radically incorrect, it being out of all reason to suppose that our present methods of cooking and general treatment of food are in any way compatible with the laws of nature.

Primarily, intestinal toxæmia owes its origin to errors in diet, and secondly, to infection which can only occur when the conditions of the gut are abnormal. This condition is present in almost all, if not every individual living on diet such as we eat. Its presence may not give rise to symptoms for months, years, or until old age, as disease depends considerably on the individual to resist poisons, though to a certain extent on the variety of the organisms connected with the toxæmia.

Abnormal diet may begin at birth, as in the case of artificial feeding, more commonly at the end of the first few months.

Considered from a natural history point of view, the human species was undoubtedly intended to live on the fruits and products of a vegetable nature of the tropics, and possibly on the flesh of the smaller animals, but whether man was intended to be a vegetarian or a carnivore one thing is certain, that our present cooking, storage, and tampering with food were not allowed for in the universal order of things.

Thus we shall see later an abnormal content in the bowel begins with us early, and persists throughout life.

It is possible that given the normal diet from birth abnormal organisms in the intestines would probably fail to become permanent residents although they are so universally present.

I am offering this paper to you for three reasons:-

(1) That an enormous number of chronic diseases can be treated successfully on these lines.

(2) That the benefit obtained is due to a general improvement in health and not to local treatment.

(3) That 25 per cent of all cases of definitely advanced inoperable cancer treated by these methods show a temporary improvement and relief of symptoms, and generally have a more comfortable time.

If 25 per cent of advanced cases of cancer show even the least sign of benefit, and it is possible to claim more than that, it appears that this line of thought and research should be worthy of further investigation.

We will now consider these points in detail, and give an outline of the results.

The deficiencies in natural food: (1) Absence in essential products necessary to health, such as vitamins, &c. (2) The lack of substances necessary for the bacterial content of the intestines to ensure cleanliness. (3) The presence of substances from which toxins can be readily made.

(1) The deficiency of vitamins and substances necessary to health is so accepted and has been so proven, that it is not necessary to discuss them in detail, bearing in mind the outstanding cases such as rickets and scurvy, and yet when more research has been done it will probably be shown that minor deficiencies extending over a long period of time have a serious effect on the general metabolism.

(2) For the intestines to be kept clean, certain organisms are necessary, and these can only exist when provided with proper food. The cleansing bacteria of the gut are the lactic acid bacilli, as from the acids they produce they prevent putrefaction, and cause a healthy and comparatively sterile excreta. Starch is essential for this process, as it is necessary to have sugars, or sugars and starch, in the cæcum to effect this process.

The average diet contains a deficiency in starch. Cooking further reduces the small amount present to be unavailing, by causing rupture of the cellulose capsule, and partial hydrolysis of the carbohydrates, so that the cæcum is hopelessly deficient in sugar from which the acid reaction may be drained.

(3) There is present an excess of flesh protein from which poisons of a toxic nature can be so readily produced.

The comparison between the fæces of those living on an average diet and of those taking a large amount of raw material has been very interesting and very striking. The average colour is darkish brown, whereas it should be pale brown. The average smell is what is described as fæcal, whereas there should be no odour, or at the most a slight smell as of sour milk.

The average reaction as described in textbooks is given as alkaline, whereas it should be strongly acid to litmus.

Chemically, most of the putrefactive bodies such as skatol and indol are absent, and finally, the bacterial content differs enormously in the two. The ordinary specimens being composed mostly of *B. coli*, streptococci, spore-bearing bacilli and abnormal bacteria, which I shall describe later, whereas the only organisms found in a healthy stool are the lactic acid bacilli and *B. coli*.

This great contrast alone should be sufficient to convince anyone of the advantages of correct diet, and the benefit the individual must obtain from the absence of all the usual putrefactive material. But there is even more than this, because in the healthy intestines that I have described abnormal bacteria can only exist with difficulty, and are unable to produce their toxins readily, whereas, the alkaline medium, as has been realized for many years in all laboratories, is an excellent breeding-ground for the majority of pathogenic bacteria, and in which alone they are unable to produce toxins.

Moreover, the natural scavenging organism of the intestine, the lactic acid bacilli, practically dies out when the cæcal content is alkaline.

We now come to those abnormal bacteria which are mostly responsible for toxæmia. These organisms are found almost universally in civilization. They are bacilli of the Gram-negative type, which do not ferment lactose. A large number of varieties of them have been worked out in detail, but the number of the different forms is so enormous that it is impossible to classify them all, and it is sufficient for the present to put them into groups. These organisms are not pathogenic in the ordinary sense of the word, in that they do not produce disease, although they may occasionally be responsible for local conditions in the intestines, but their danger lies in their prolonged, continued action, and the toxins which they are slowly producing throughout life, gradually and insidiously lowering the vitality of the individual, and giving increased susceptibility to both acute and chronic disease. According to the virulence of the toxæmia, and possibly equally important according to the resistance of the host, so depend the number of years necessary before symptoms are developed. In most cases the human subject becomes infected early in life, and so commonly are these organisms found, not only in the adult, but also in the child, that they might be considered, as they even are in some laboratories, as more or less normal inhabitants, were it not for the dramatic results obtained in the treatment of chronic disease by their removal.

Once having gained entrance to the body, they appear to live in the region of the gall-bladder and bile-ducts, and the Americans have amply demonstrated this by obtaining them in a large percentage of cases by passing a bougie down through the mouth and stomach into the duodenum.

Treatment consists of two distinct parts, with the object in view of removing the intestinal toxæmia. On the one hand the diet should be so arranged as to contain the least possible amount of material from which toxins can be manufactured, and most suitable for the growth of scavenging bacteria and inhibition of abnormal organisms; and, secondly, to remove the toxin-producing bacteria from the patient. The diet consists in removing all forms of cooked flesh, as it is from this poisons are so readily produced, and keeping the patient almost completely on a vegetable, fruit, nut, and cereal diet.

This alone enormously reduces the amount of toxins produced in the intestines; also, if continued for a long period, ultimately tends to remove pathogenic bacteria, but unfortunately in the majority of cases this process takes years to accomplish, as the toxins appear to obtain hold, probably in the gall-bladder and bile-ducts, exactly in the same way as has been so frequently proved in typhoid carriers.

The removal of these oganisms is therefore not easy. Intestinal antiseptics for a time have beneficial results, but not of a permanent nature.

Correct diet, as I have just said, is a very long process. Vaccine therapy appears to give the best results. For this purpose vaccines must be given with the greatest caution, as they have a very profound effect on the system, and unless given in a scientific way may do harm.

After the dose, which should be the smallest possible which will give a result, there should be an aggravation of all symptoms, which under ideal conditions last one or two days, but in more profound cases may persist for a month.

After this aggravation improvement should occur, and so long as any improvement whatever is taking place, even if it be a year, no further dose should be administered. On these lines it is extra-ordinary, even in severe cases of chronic disease, how a few doses may effect a cure.

I have given you an outline of the conditions of a toxic intestine. The difference of the average excreta and the clean wholesome fæces of a natural diet, without putrefaction or odour, obviously must have an enormous influence on the individual, also the completely different flora which is to be found, must be convincing; but to be really able to appreciate the importance of the removal of a toxic condition it is necessary, as many have done in the last several years, to witness many cases so treated and the remarkable benefit obtained.

This condition is not the actual exciting cause of disease, but by its insidious action, extended over months or years it lowers the vitality and resistance, allowing the possibility of infection due to the presence of the true exciting cause. The removal of this condition allows the body to fight in a most efficient and surprising way even advanced disease itself. The tubercle bacillus is mostly accepted as the cause of consumption, yet how little has the discovery of that germ helped to fight the disease, except by guarding from infection.

The tubercle bacillus itself is unable to become dangerous except under the conditions of a lowered vitality, and in most cases of consumption much benefit is obtained, even after the disease is well established, by the removal of the underlying toxæmia. So as in consumption, this applies to a large number of the chronic diseases, the general treatment being to improve the condition of the patient, and the individual will then cure himself of the local condition, and one of the surest methods of raising resistance and causing a general improvement is by cleansing the intestines and relieving the body of the poisons so usually generated therein.

It will interest you to know that from experiments that have been done many remedies of a more deeply acting nature have a profound effect on these abnormal bacteria of which I have been talking, and it has been demonstrated that their action is similar in every way to the result of an injection of vaccine.

The benefit obtained on the lines I have described in chronic disease is too widely established, and has been practised and observed over many years by too many medical men to be any longer in doubt. And now for malignant disease.

There is a growing tendency throughout the laboratories of the world to suspect diet as a predisposing cause to cancer; many various modifications of food have been tried, in some cases with distinctly favourable results; my own experience during the last eight years, on those cases which I have had the opportunity of treating, is that without claiming a single cure, 25 per cent of advanced, and mostly very advanced, cases received temporary and definite benefit.

Our object is not to cure cancer, our aim being to prevent. And if the removal of intestinal toxæmia can so improve even the most advanced cases, how much more should its absence throughout life completely prevent the occurrence of this dread disease? Most of the cases with which I have dealt have been in the last stages, and in many also diet has been impossible for economic reasons when connected with institutions, so that if one took the percentage of benefit in private cases only it would be very much larger.

I will now give you a few examples of some of the best results that have been obtained; nothing miraculous, but you must remember that they were all terminal cases, and that the consistency of the results has been far too steady to make any chance of coincidence possible.

Case 1. – Mrs F.C., aged 37. March, 1923. Had breast removed two years previously. Present condition, growth in both lungs and liver. Effusion in both pleuræ. Sternum markedly bulging; continuous vomiting: pulse 130; respirations 32. First dose, March 16: Marked benefit after twenty-four hours. General improvement continued for three weeks. Second dose, April 5: More marked improvement; patient able to get up. Improvement continued, and after a few weeks patient leading an almost normal life. Respirations and pulse becoming normal; and the fluid diminished. No increase in size of growth. Third dose, June 15: Steady improvement through June, July, August and September. Patient did moderately well till the middle of December; she was taken suddenly ill December 27 and died on the 28th.

Case 2. – Mr J.B., aged 63. Solicitor. Carcinoma of gall-bladder and liver. December, 1919, patient in great pain and distress. Huge mass of liver. Morphia necessary for pain. First dose, December: Relief of pain within forty-eight hours. General improvement followed during the next three weeks. At the end of a month patient up and about, and resumed his duties which he continued until July. During this time the growth slightly diminished in size; but the pain and distress entirely disappeared. Two further doses were given. In August the patient was suddenly taken ill with apparent heart failure, and died within three weeks.

Case 3. – Mr W.S., aged 72. Carcinoma of the tongue. Tongue had been removed and an extensive growth in the floor of the mouth and the glands of the neck. Considerable pain and frequent small hæmorrhage from the mouth. First dose, November 7: The pain and hæmorrhage both ceased twenty-four hours after the dose. The growth became cleaner. Other doses were given on December 14, January 29, and February 18. There was no further pain nor hæmorrhage. The growth remained stationary until February, when it started to enlarge slightly. Patient died suddenly on March 1.

Case 4. – Mrs M.R., aged 66. Advanced carcinoma of the cervix. Considerable hæmorrhage and some pain. First dose, October 25: Hæmorrhage and pain ceased until December. Second dose, December 9: General condition improved. Slight hæmorrhage January 15. Third dose given: General improvement up to May. Not quite so well. Fourth dose, June 5: Patient still alive and slightly better.

Case 5. – Mrs E.M., aged 62. Advanced carcinoma of the cervix. Confined to bed. Considerable pain and distress. Sedatives being given. First dose, February 15: Considerable improvement. After a week patient was able to be about. Second dose given in March and the third in June. Patient's condition is still very fair, and she is able to be about and assist in the doing of ward-work.

It would be possible to continue citing such cases indefinitely, and such are the average results of those cases which respond well: diminished pain, frequently completely absent, and an improvement of all symptoms, with a more or less shrinkage in the growth, the patient being rendered more comfortable, and the end when it comes generally being sudden or after a short relapse.

The fundamental points which I want to bring home are:

(1) That civilized diet is unnatural, deficient in necessary properties for health, and also to ensure the intestines being able to be kept in a clean state.

(2) That the conditions which arise in the bowel as a result of this allow an abnormal flora, an absence of the purifying organisms, and the presence of toxin-producing bacteria, with the result that the fæces are objectionable and dangerous.

(3) That removal of this condition, and cleansing of the gut, causes a most remarkable improvement in the general health, and usually

also in most chronic diseases, without any local treatment.

(4) And finally from the work done there seems to be hope that this most simple remedy would reduce the incidence of malignant disease, and even be useful, when more thoroughly worked out, in the treatment of the disease when established.

Intestinal poisoning is no longer the vague apparition of the past, when stasis alone was supposed to be the main cause. We now know the necessary diet to eliminate the foods from which toxins are most readily formed, the bacteria concerned in its production and the toxins themselves can be isolated.

Toxæmia depends not so much on stasis as the content of the gut; if no poisons be present, even when stasis exists, naturally there can be no absorption; but if the fæces are foul no matter how rapidly they pass there will be a certain amount of absorption into the bloodstream.

Usually when the condition of the intestinal content becomes clean, there is such an improvement in muscular tone and general health that constipation ceases.

– XIX –

The Relation of Vaccine Therapy to Homœopathy

[*British Homœopathic Journal*, April 1920]

Mr PRESIDENT, – May I by way of introduction tell you how proud I am to be invited to read a paper before your Society? Though a comparative junior, I have been studying allopathic medicine for thirteen years, and have been practising with one of the foremost hospitals in London for seven years before I was appointed here last March, so that I have had a fair chance of studying allopathic medicine and its possibilities. It is impossible for me to tell you how deeply I have been impressed with the science of homœopathy and with the results you obtain.

As one who has had the opportunity of witnessing the results, and even working with some of the present foremost physicians of the old school, and as one who has seen enough of medicine to realize value, and as one who has had enough experience to make one sceptical of all things, may I offer my allopathic offering at the altar of your science by saying that you accomplish cures undreamed of by the profession at large; that a large class of cases considered almost hopeless by the allopaths are amongst the most brilliant of your successes; that your results are such as no other London hospital can attempt to equal; and lastly, that words fail to describe the wonder and genius of Hahnemann, a giant in medicine whose equal has never existed.

It seems incredible that one man alone, in the dark ages of medicine a hundred years ago, could have discovered the hitherto inconceived science of the like remedy, not only also the power of the potentized dose, but, in addition, the perfect method of administering doses.

It seems equally incredible that any medical scientist could read the *Organon* of Hahnemann without realizing that he was reading the work of a great master. The shrewd observation of facts, the faithful recording of results, and the masterly deductions arrived at there-from, deductions which science is rediscovering today after a century's work, would make the *Organon* an extraordinary book if it had been written at the present time.

This evening I want to discuss the relation of vaccines to homœopathy. Before I start I want to mention two things. First, I do not in any way wish to make any comparisons between homœopathic and vaccine therapy. My sole wish is to show that vaccines are a modern branch of medical science extraordinarily closely related to your own methods, and, on account of the good results obtained, may be worthy of consideration as a modern confirmation of the truths of homœopathy. Secondly, I do not want to judge vaccines by the general opinion of them as they are used today. Broadly speaking, they are a hopeless failure compared with what they should be, and this is due to the following causes. The preparations of vaccines are so often undertaken by those who are ignorant of the correct methods, and the result is a very inferior article. As an example, take the trade vaccines, made by the large firms on an enormous scale; these are generally made from what are known as sub-cultures, that is organisms which have been grown primarily direct from the pathological lesion on to culture media; they are then regrown on other culture media, often many times in succession, the object being, of course, to obtain a greater yield. A tube of organisms may come from Paris or America and be sown on to hundreds more, until the organism has been so badly treated by these unnatural methods that the organisms of the last cultures would hardly recognise those of the first culture, so altered have the become – not in shape, but in virulence and pathological possibilities.

Now, the expert knows that primary cultures alone – that is only cultures grown from the pathological material – are of the best value. Such as I have mentioned and other gross errors enormously reduce the efficiency of vaccines as supplied to the medical market. Then, again, the practitioner using the vaccine often knows nothing of the laws and indications of vaccine therapy. He obtains the dose from a chemist or bacteriologist, with the minimum of directions, blindly pushes in doses which would make the expert tear his hair, repeats the wrong dose either too soon or too late, and, to say the least of it, gets a very poor result, and sometimes even it would have been better for the patients had vaccines never been invented. When you consider that vaccines require every bit as much care and expert management in while such a hopeless confusion exists, that the results are such as to give grave doubts of their value to the profession. The case is similar to your telling an allopathic physician to give arsenic without giving him further instructions.

The resemblance of vaccine therapy to homœopathy is very close, so close that it is more a question: are they not identical? I want to discuss the resemblance according to the following heads:

(1) The nature of the substance used.
(2) The dose.
(3) Isopathic or homœopathic.
(4) Necessity for like remedy.
(5) The types of remedies.
(6) The methods of use.

NATURE OF THE REMEDY

Homœopathic remedies are of three types:

(1) Animal and insect poisons.
(2) Vegetable juices.
(3) Inorganic substances and their salts.

Let us take No. 1 first. The poisons of animals and insects are practically certain toxic substances which are derived from protein, generally split up into its highest derivatives. They are albumoses and proteoses. Such substances we now know to be extremely similar to or identical with the toxins of bacteria. It would be quite impossible chemically to distinguish between the proteose poison of the snake and the toxin of diphtheria. These poisons may account for anaphylaxis, and can cause death more rapidly when suitably administered than strychnine or prussic acid. Thus this class of remedies we see to be extraordinarily close to or identical with the toxins of bacteria.

The second class, vegetable juices. Here also is ground for thought. Bacteria are protein in nature, moreover vegetable protein, so that again there must be a close relationship between vegetable juices and vaccines. It is not inconceivable that the remedy of a particular case may be the drug which most closely corresponds to the toxin causing the disease, and in some way neutralizing the poison or stimulating the body to overcome its effects. The third group are more difficult to allocate or classify.

Whilst several elements, as sodium, potassium, carbon, &c., are represented in bacterial protein, there are some, as zinc or lead, which, as far as is known, never enter into the composition of vaccines. Even here the discrepancy may not be as much as first appears, since elements like phosphorus present in protein may represent its group, including arsenic and antimony. Hence, with the exception of the comparatively small number included in group 3, there is at once a striking resemblance even in the compositions of remedies and vaccines.

THE DOSE

Vaccines have been proved to have a beneficial effect when potentized; this applies not only to autogenous vaccines when prepared for special cases, but also stock remedies such as influenzinum, medorrhinum, tuberculin, &c. When so used the size of the dose is homœopathic, thus vaccines are able to effect their cure in such doses. In vaccines given in the usual way by hypodermic syringe, the dose is larger, but even then the total amount is very small. For instance, the total weight of *B. coli*, given as a usual initial dose, would be about 1/200000 mgm, which would correspond to about the 7 or 8x potency of arsenic. Again, by the method of preparing vaccines it is impossible to avoid potentizing them to a certain extent, and, as I have just said, to about 7 or 8x, so that potentization plays some part. Another resemblance is the point that the perfect dose varies greatly in different cases; one case of septicæmia, for instance, may react perfectly to a dose of 5 mill or 10 mill streptococci, another case similar in other respects, requiring 20 or 30 mill, or more. Also in chronic diseases some patients react markedly to 1 mill of their intestinal organisms, even alarmingly, others requiring 10 or 20 mill to give the same response.

HOMŒOPATHIC OR ISOPATHIC

It is open to much argument as to which of the above classes vaccines belong. They are certainly not isopathic, because in their preparation they have lost certain characters of their original state; the organisms are unable to reproduce, or to produce toxins, &c. (2) The organisms in a vaccine are so changed that they are unable to produce the disease which they originally caused, although, like homœopathic remedies, they are able to produce certain symptoms. No matter how much typhoid vaccine was given to an individual, the disease would not be produced, although headache, backache and temperature would arise from a comparatively small dose. (3) Again, organisms very closely allied to the causative germ of a particular disease may give benefit when used as a vaccine, thus any of the large number of varieties of the streptococci will be beneficial in an infection with a particular streptococcus, so much so that stock strains are almost always used in acute cases, though the different varieties have different characters, as may be shown in their size, shape, and their fermentation when tested on different sugars. Again, immunizing with typhoid organisms produces a certain amount of resistance to paratyphoid and other closely allied bacilli, and the blood of patients who have had typhoid or have been inoculated against it will agglutinate the sera of dysentery or paratyphoid bacilli.

NECESSITY FOR LIKE REMEDY

In vaccine therapy, as in homœopathy, the remedy must be like. It would be useless to use a streptococcus to cure typhoid, or a staphylococcus for dysentery; the vaccine must contain germs identical or very closely allied to the causative organism.

THE RESULT OF A DOSE

Here we see the most striking analogy between the sets of remedies. (1) The reaction to a dose is enormously greater in susceptible than in non-susceptible patients. If a medicinal potentized dose of sepia be given to a normal individual, practically nothing happens, but in a patient suffering from sepia symptoms the same dose will have a profound influence. So in vaccines a normal individual can tolerate a dose of 100 mill streptococci with little or no discomfort; but if a patient suffering from streptococcic pneumonia were given a similar dose he would have a violent reaction, which in many cases would be fatal. In typhoid, 500 or 1,000 mill bacilli are given to the normal individual as a prophylactic dose, but in treating a patient with the disease a hundredth, or even a thousandth, of that dose would be used. (2) In disease also our comparison holds; the results of a dose of vaccine is: If dose is too small nothing happens, or a slight amelioration; if dose is perfect, complete amelioration; if slightly too large, small aggravation, then amelioration; if much too large, continued aggravation. If a hundred cases of pneumonia received a usual first dose of vaccine, in some the temperature would fall to the normal in six to eight hours, the perfect dose for those cases; in some there would be a slight rise, then fall; in some a small fall of temperature only, and in some no change.

In vaccine therapy we know that any of the above sequences depend on the size of the dose, and all we have to do is to find the perfect amount; there is no question of the wrong remedy when the vaccine is prepared from the patient, or the organism has been identified. Any such result may follow a homœopathic dose. In vaccines we have one important sign which materially assists in judging the correctness of a given dose, namely, the local reaction, that is, the hyperæmia which occurs at the site of inoculation, and which if perfect is about the size of half-a-crown; a local reaction of less that this usually means an overdose; if larger, the converse. This local reaction also assists in determining the time for repeating the dose, since as long as the local reaction continues to be visible it may be taken for granted that the dose is still working. In acute cases any rise of temperature will be associated with the disappearance of the local hyperæmia.

In vaccines one of the greatest difficulties is to estimate the initial dose, because the size necessary to give the perfect result varies widely in different cases. It is therefore wise always to give a dose which is likely to be on the small side, because we know no antidotes, should a severe reaction occur. It is always easier, if after a few hours the primary dose is seen to be too small, to repeat a larger dose than to overcome the effects of an overdose.

Methods of Use

Again here the laws are identical, and if all bacteriologists would closely adhere to the rules laid down by Hahnemann, vaccines would be infinitely more beneficial than given, alas! as they so often are, by some routine method, as once a week or some every ten days. The guide in repeating a vaccine dose is "Never repeat until certain that improvement has ceased, whether it be after ten or twelve hours or so in acute cases, or after weeks or months in chronic disease." It is through ignoring this fundamental principle that many a practitioner has given up vaccine as useless.

The physician who repeats a pneumonia vaccine whilst the temperature is falling as a result of the first dose, does so not only at the risk of losing all value of dose number one, but often takes the chance of the patient's life. In chronic disease, many a promising case which has started to definitely improve has had all the chances ruined by hasty repetition. Then, again, vaccines in acute cases, if there is need for repeating, may be given every eight hours, or so, whilst chronic cases, weeks or months must elapse before repetition can be safely undertaken.

TYPES OF REMEDIES

There are two distinct types of vaccines, acute and chronic. In acute diseases the organism necessary for the cure is the particular germ found in the local lesion causing the disease. Thus in pneumonia the sputum provides the correct germ; in cystitis the urine, in abscess the pus, and so on; and the inoculation of a vaccine made from the source will effect the cure providing the case has not advanced too far.

In chronic disease it is totally different; in such cases we are dealing not only with local lesions, whatever they may be, but also with a profound underlying cause which renders the individual susceptible to prolonged disease. This cause is found in a chronic poisoning from various organisms which live in the intestinal tract, so that in disease the aim is to rid the individual of the intestinal organisms and their toxins. It is remarkable in old cases how, after such toxins have been removed by a vaccine, the chronic illness disappears and local lesions of ten or many years' standing entirely clear up. How like this is to the types of homœopathic remedies.

Bacterial intestinal toxæmia is most interesting and important. If the stools of individuals suffering from disease are examined, certain organisms are found which may be considered to be abnormal, and from various symptoms of the patient one is able to predict to a certain extent what type of organism would be isolated. Thus, individuals having unusual fears, such as dread of fire, heights, crowds, traffic, have almost invariably an organism of the paratyphoid group of bacilli. The highly-strung, nervy person with anxious expression, often with a fixed look, frequently has a bacillus of the proteus group. The patient who at a casual glance appears to be in perfect health and yet has some serious chronic disease such as tubercle, often has organisms of the coli mutable group. The folk who bruise and bleed easily generally possess a dysentery type of germ, and so on. If a vaccine of the organism isolated from one of these patients be given, the result is typically homœopathic, as follows.

A latent period of four hours to six or seven days follows the dose, then the reaction or aggravation of every symptom present in the patient results, lasting from twelve hours to four or five days, or sometimes longer. This is followed by amelioration of all symptoms, commencing with those which were the last to appear during the disease, though during this period older symptoms in the history of the case, which may for a long time have been latent, may manifest themselves, finally to disappear. In cases of rheumatoid arthritis and neuritis, I have several times seen pains come out during this period which the patients state they have not had since childhood; such symptoms enable one to tell the patient with confidence that a complete cure is at hand. To take epilepsy as an example, after the first dose, although it be given at a time when by previous experience no attack is anticipated, a fit usually results corresponding to the aggravation, or, as we call it, reaction; this is followed by an interval which is longer than usual for the patient to be free from attacks, and the second dose is not given until an attack or threatened attack takes place.

There are also points in common as regards the aggravation between vaccines and remedies. After a vaccine the ideal reaction is a short one; no reaction, generally speaking, means no response and no curative value; a prolonged reaction always means that the case is going to be of a difficult nature. I do not know your opinion as regards the following point, but after vaccines I personally always prefer to have a short aggravation rather than to have an instant amelioration, as with few exceptions I believe the cure in the former case to be more complete.

Intestinal toxæemia corresponds in the most remarkable manner to the Hahnemann psora. All that wonderful list of symptoms, such as weariness, loss of appetite, pallor, loss of energy, nervous twitchings, which he describes as being present in an individual who is not ill, according to the general sense, and who on going to a physician would be that he was neurotic and only wanted a change of air, being constitutionally sound. All those symptoms, which are really precursors and symptoms of early definite disease can be proved to be due to this chronic poison from the intestine; and when the poison is removed the patient rapidly loses all these minor symptoms. More-over, in disease itself, if this underlying toxæmia can be cut off, there is no need for tonics, stimulants or rest; providing the disease is not too far advanced, nature, freed from the poison, will be soon quite capable of eradicating all the lesions.

It is surprising in cases of chronic disease how, after two or three doses of a vaccine obtained from a single organism in the intestine, the whole condition improves and the patient becomes well. I have seen a case of psoriasis of seven years' standing disappear after two doses, and an epilepsy of twenty years' standing, having attacks every month, go for over twelve months free of attacks as a result of one inoculation. It is vaccines of this type that correspond most closely to your long-acting antipsoric drugs. In acute disease, of course, there is need for an antipsoric remedy, but, like you, the patient has to be saved from the acute state by quick-acting vaccines, that is vaccines made from the local lesion; and afterwards attention can be paid to the long-acting vaccines as a precaution against further infection. It would be quite useless to give one of these intestinal toxic vaccines in pneumonia, for example, because the patient would probably be dead long before the benefit of the vaccine could be felt. But having saved your patient by an inoculation of pneumococci or streptococci made from the sputum, after convalescence it is well to find the intestinal organism and give doses which will raise the *general resistance against disease* in all forms. Thus I have attempted to point out to you the extraordinary resemblance of the most modern branch of medical science to the teachings of homœopathy: in composition; in the size of the dose; in the result of a dose; in the methods of use; in the types of remedies. All through we see that there are so many characters in common. Science may go further yet. It may prove that the remedies of your school correspond in ways yet unknown to the various poisons of the body in disease; it may show that the particular remedy for a certain set of symptoms is the one most closely corres-ponding to the toxin or poison causing these symptoms; it may even show in time in what manner the remedies act and how they are able to neutralize, or stimulate the body to neutralize, the poisons.

Meanwhile it should be realized that science in a totally different manner is confirming the principles of homœopathy. To Hahnemann should fall all the honour for having anticipated science by more than a century.

The attitude today of the medical profession in general is one of regard towards homœopathy; but when, as is shortly certain to happen, it is generally recognized and appreciated that all modern research at the hands of the allopaths is rapidly proving and drifting in the direction of Hahnemann's laws, then will homœopathy be acknowledged to be the wonderful science that it is.

Let all the members of your Society see to it that they are proud to be amongst the pioneers; let them see to it that they do not err one jot from the fundamental laws of their great founder. For science is proving him in detail – the like remedy, the single dose, the danger of hasty repetition.

It is going to be a struggle between the old homœopathy and the new; see to it that the old receives its due share of credit, that its standard is kept high, and, true to its teachings, that it is not swamped in the flood of science which is merely following in the wake of Hahnemann.

— ✗ —